Putting Tiny Patients First

Putting Tiny Patients First

A Life in Paediatrics

Herbert Barrie

Edited By Michael Barrie

Matador
9 Priory Business Park,
Wistow Road, Kibworth Beauchamp,
Leicestershire. LE8 0RX
Tel: 0116 279 2299
Email: books@troubador.co.uk
Web: www.troubador.co.uk/matador
Twitter: @matadorbooks

ISBN 978 1789014 167

British Library Cataloguing in Publication Data.
A catalogue record for this book is available from the British Library.

Printed and bound by CPI Group (UK) Ltd, Croydon, CR0 4YY
Typeset in 11.5 Sabon by Troubador Publishing Ltd, Leicester, UK

Matador is an imprint of Troubador Publishing Ltd

*This book is dedicated to all those babies who could have survived had there been a better understanding of the principles and practice of resuscitation.
They were denied the chance of life.*

Contents

Dr Herbert Barrie was head of the department of child health at Charing Cross Hospital. He was a pioneer in neonatology and the care of the preterm infant – in particular resuscitation of the newborn. At Charing Cross Hospital, he developed one of the first special care baby units in London. The unit that he built, and ran, was innovative and set the scene for neonatal intensive care across the country. He also developed the country's first neonatal ambulance.

They say that the medical profession needs its physicians to be clever, the public expects them to be kind, and students hope for a clear and wise teacher. Herbert Barrie was all these things and more.

This book tells of his life through his published work, anecdotes and selected correspondence.

Acknowledgements

I am very grateful to Joe Ruston, Dr Angela Bennett, Dr Bashir Qureshi, Lesley Agutter, Sally Vinter and Dr Peter Husband for their lucid and warm tributes and for their words of kindness. Thank you, too, to Elizabeth Aspel for her moving tribute: she was a source of great encouragement to my father when he relocated his neonatal unit, and to me too when I was compiling this book.

Anne Barker wrote a heartfelt piece in *The Times* recounting my father's involvement in the early care of her four daughters; she unwittingly provided the perfect title for this book.

I am grateful to the publishers of *The Lancet* for allowing me to reproduce written material that originally appeared in their In England Now columns. Likewise I am very grateful to Dr Frederick Rivara, Editor-in-Chief, *JAMA Pediatrics*, for graciously allowing me to reproduce my father's articles that first appeared in the *American Journal of Diseases of Children*. Copyright of these articles remains with the American Medical Association.

I am indebted to my father's close friend Chris Prance who very generously allowed me to reproduce emails and letters that they exchanged over many years.

A big 'thank you' to Ben and Hildegard Croucher for patiently and expertly typing up the manuscript. I would have been lost without you both.

I had lots of help with the photographs: thank you to my wonderful sons, Robert and Alex, for patiently adapting pre-digital photographs to a modern format. Likewise to Neil Rhodes, a professional photo-restorer, whose skill has made a world of difference to many of the photographs. And to Niki at Haria Pharmacy for helping me, usually at short notice!

I am grateful to Dr Dhiren Shah. Your daily telephone calls during Dad's final illness were a source of comfort and succour at a time when it was most needed. You are a true friend.

And finally, thank you to my wife Roopal and to my sons, Robert and Alex. Roopal, you were like a second daughter to Dad. He thought the world of you. Robert and Alex: your grandfather loved you both more than words can ever say. You carry into the future not just your grandfather's story, but also his spirit of hope and perseverance.

Michael Barrie

Introduction

Writing a synopsis of someone's life is a difficult undertaking; when that person is your father the task is no easier. Herbert Barrie was many things to different people: a paediatrician, a doctor, a colleague, an innovator, a friend. To me he was Dad. Of course growing up I was aware of his medical career and the professional life he led in paediatrics and, in particular, neonatology. How could I do otherwise? Long days that stretched into evenings spent in the hospital, arriving home after my sister and I had gone to bed; weekends spent at the neonatal unit; the phone calls in the night summoning him back in.

It was not until after Dad died that I fully appreciated the impact he had, not just on those whose lives he touched directly, but also in the care of the newborn infant. Indeed, my father was among the first wave of paediatricians in the United Kingdom to look after the very youngest of their patients, namely babies.

Dad was born in Berlin on 9th October 1927. His parents were Jewish: his mother, Ida, was from Lwów, Galicia, then part of the Austro-Hungarian Empire, and his father, Emil Bihari, was from Budapest, Hungary. In the early stages of World War I, Lwów was captured by the Russians; Emil was a soldier in the Austro-Hungarian Army which had been sent, in 1915, from Budapest to recapture Galicia.

In my father's own words: *My mother came from Czernica, a tiny village on the River Dniester near Lwów. The name is common to half a dozen villages in Poland but the nearest station was Piaczetzna, a twenty-minute horse-carriage drive away. She was fluent in three languages, told fortunes from cards so accurately that she refused to do so for fear of imparting bad news, and was full of wise sayings like 'Think of good and good will come', which were guaranteed to make my father erupt in explosions of Hungarian invective.*

Back to the story. Emil and his troops were due to be moved west after six months. Ida's father said to his young daughter, 'Don't worry – there'll be other men.'

'But he's coming back to marry me!' said Ida indignantly.

Ida's father rolled his eyes. '*Oy, ir vet keynmol zen im vider,*' he said, which is Yiddish for 'Oh, you'll never see him again.'

But Emil did return. He retraced his earlier route through Poland until he found Ida. Emil took his new bride back to Budapest, which was not a happy occasion because she could not speak a word of Hungarian.

Emil sensed his new wife's discomfort and so applied for work in Berlin (where his brother was living with his wife and daughter). Their first son, Julian, was born in 1925, followed two years later by Herbert.

All was going well and the boys enjoyed their childhood until the Nazis came to power. At the end of 1936 the family fled Nazi Germany and came to England. Their first home was in a block of flats built around a tennis court. This sparked a lifelong passion for tennis.

We arrived in London in December. My father had spent the previous six months there desperately trying to secure a job as a transformer designer, his profession before Hitler came to power; to learn English; and to prepare the ground for us to come over. I was sworn to strict secrecy about his whereabouts in case it should go wrong. He was helped by a Jewish organisation in Woburn Square which probably accounted for a lasting debt of gratitude by helping other refugees. For example, we fostered a little girl, Doris Spitz, from Klagenfurt after the Anschluss until her parents (temporary cook and gardener to a big house in Surrey) were properly settled.

I was never victimised in Berlin by antisemitism personally. I attended school normally, my best friend was the daughter of a 'Brown-shirt', complete with jackboots, and we were in and out of each other's flats freely. The owner and other tenants in the block were decency and kindness personified and saw us off at the station with tears in their eyes. Another couple who owned a cinema gave me and my brother free tickets every Saturday morning with instructions to the usherette to offer us anything we wanted from her tray in the interval.

Then we fled to England. My parents breathed a huge sigh of relief as we crossed the border. I was violently sick on the ferry crossing and remember thinking how cold and wet it was when we eventually docked in Harwich. We put up in a cheap hotel near Victoria Station for a week until our furniture arrived. A strident, barbaric noise awoke me every night – kilted buskers playing bagpipes, as it turned out – and I gagged on bitter marmalade at the first breakfast, mistaking it for apricot jam. We settled in a flat in Carshalton, a short bus ride for my father to his office in Hackbridge. The flats were built round a square with a tennis court and this started a love affair with tennis.

Dad rarely spoke of his childhood: the few paragraphs above are a rare contemplation of his early years. His family, which spanned Poland, Ukraine, Germany and then England of the 20th century, suffered from the collective amnesia that followed in Eastern Europe after it was ransacked of its Jewish population during the Second World War. Neither he, his brother, nor his parents were religious. In fact Dad was an atheist, although he never openly declared this. I just knew. After the war, Emil made enquiries through the Red Cross as to the fate of the family left behind in Poland (now Ukraine), Hungary and Germany. Twelve close family members, including Emil's brother, sister-in-law and niece, and Ida's parents and siblings, had perished in the Holocaust. This tragic news must have had an impact on my father and may well explain his lack of any religious belief.

At the age of eleven, Dad won a scholarship to Wallington County Grammar School and from there went on to University College Hospital Medical School, London. Julian, his brother, was already studying medicine there. Dad qualified as a doctor in 1950. In his final year at medical school he changed his surname to Barrie.

As a child, my father almost died from a bout of streptococcal septicaemia and, inspired by the care shown by his doctors, resolved to become a children's doctor. His interest in the fledgling specialty of paediatrics led him to Great Ormond Street Hospital for Children, followed by a year as research fellow at Harvard University and the Children's Medical Center in Boston, Massachusetts.

Many years later, recalling his time in the United States, he wrote to a friend, saying, *I am reminded of a visit I paid to the paediatric ward at the Sloan Kettering Hospital in New York in 1957. At intervals on every wall was a picture of a large, pink human ear. The reason, I was told, was to protect the children (and their parents) from careless talk about their illness. This was just one tiny aspect of their impressive approach to the challenge of paediatrics even then.*

In 1959 Dad was appointed senior registrar, then five years later senior lecturer, at St Thomas's Hospital, London. Colleagues described him as organised, systematic and a creative thinker. It was at St Thomas's that he first developed a profound interest in the care of premature infants. This was a time of rapid medical advances, particularly in respiratory support, that were at last making the survival of premature babies a reality. Very few babies born before thirty-two weeks survived, and those who did often suffered neurological impairment.

When I was a student and then a house officer, the premature baby unit didn't exist. Only a linen cupboard kept by a sister with green fingers. If she thought a baby needed special care, that was where the baby went.

Dad was troubled that many newborn infants could have survived the stress of birth had there been a better understanding of the dynamics of fetal and neonatal circulation and respiration, and even a basic knowledge of resuscitation. Today the majority of premature newborns survive thanks to the collaborative efforts of the neonatologist, the medical scientist, the physiologist and the epidemiologist in providing sound measures not only for the prompt detection and treatment of respiratory distress, but more so for preventing it from happening in the first place.

Dad pioneered advances in resuscitation of the newborn, publishing his seminal paper on the subject in *The Lancet* in 1963. A film showing the practicalities of resuscitating a preterm infant was shown around the country.

One of the concerns at the time was the worry that using high pressures of oxygen could be damaging to newborn lungs. To counter this, Dad developed an underwater safety valve in the oxygen circuit. The tubes were originally made of rubber, but these had the potential to cause irritation to sensitive newborn tracheas: Dad therefore switched to plastic which was taken from a pre-cut roll and so had an inherent curvature. This plastic tube, based on his design, was known as the 'St Thomas's tube'.

Did my father's formative years have a bearing on his work in neonatology? Did his 'experience' (to employ a modern adjective) of what happened to his family impact, and ultimately influence, his zealous need to ensure the survival of babies who would otherwise have died? I'm not looking for a story-within-a-story because to do so might be obtuse and may well be mistaken. Yet researchers have spoken of second-generation Holocaust survivors possessing tenacity and enormous resolve, sometimes bordering on obstinacy. Dad did exhibit these traits, and they were best exemplified in his steadfast devotion to the premature babies under his care.

My father's time at St Thomas's was probably the happiest time of his professional life. It was during his seven years at St Thomas's that he met, and then married, my mother, Dr Dinah Castle.

In 1966, Dad was appointed consultant paediatrician to the new Charing Cross Hospital in Fulham, which was in the process of moving from The Strand. The incumbent paediatrician was Hugh Jolly, a larger-than-life character with boundless enthusiasm who espoused the rights of parents and the 'whole child'. Innovative, certainly, but Jolly was not always an easy man to work with. Dad found this an enormous contrast to his earlier years at St Thomas's where he had enjoyed being part of a superbly cohesive and tight-knit department.

Dad continued his groundbreaking work in the care of the preterm infant. There was no special care baby unit at Charing Cross, so he developed one. It was a 'baby' in its own right, and of his own making.

His special care baby unit became a hot-bed of innovation and expertise. It incorporated state-of-the art equipment and was ably equipped to handle the hospital's premature births. Those familiar with British hospitals of the post-war generation will know that much of the building stock then was composed of 'prefabs'. Dad's first neonatal unit at Charing Cross was such a building. But it was his unit and he was pleased with the successes that it achieved. It was the very first neonatal unit at Charing Cross Hospital and one of only two or three in the country (one of the others being the unit he had developed at St Thomas's).

And then tragedy struck: one fine summer's day in 1979 an unexpected downpour came crashing through the flimsy roof of the neonatal unit, causing enormous damage to electric fittings and equipment. The unit was swiftly evacuated to a spare room on the general paediatric ward – a temporary but wholly unsatisfactory situation. The room was directly off a main corridor; there was an obvious risk of infection; it was overcrowded; and it did not have piped oxygen.

The desperate search for a new home for the unit came to an end when my father chanced upon three large, empty nurseries in the very maternity hospital where the premature babies were born. The maternity department at Charing Cross was half a mile down the road at the West London Hospital. The siting of a special care baby unit in a building in which no babies had ever been born had long been a source of regret. Now there was a golden opportunity to open a brand-new unit in the very same building which housed the maternity wing. Surely, my father reasoned, it would be straightforward to move the incubators, equipment, resuscitation paraphernalia and neonatal staff across to the new site? There was ample space, too, to enlarge the capacity of the unit. More incubators meant more lives saved.

NHS bureaucracy now swung its wearisome head into full play. In what proved to be a prevailing theme throughout his consultant career, Dad now found himself up against small-minded bureaucracy. And nowhere was this more apparent than in the National Health Service. He railed against it – constantly. Just about everything was bound by a needless hierarchy of rules, duties and authority. Hospital management committees left, right and centre. Dad was no committee man: he regarded them as inefficient, wasteful and unreliable; he inveighed against hospital administrators who seemed to obstruct progress at every turn. And now they were determined to hinder the chance to move the special care baby unit.

Endless committees discussed the viability of the move. Their action was invariably slow and unwieldy compared to Dad's eagerness to 'just make it happen'. My father was unselfish but also could be stubborn, and undoubtedly fomented the situation by his intransigence. Malcolm Levene was at that time starting his first job in paediatrics at Charing Cross Hospital. He recalls that my father was 'an individualistic man who liked to plough his own furrow: a man confident in his own ability to solve problems'.

Dad alerted the national press. He told them about the awful conditions in the unit, still housed in a room on a children's ward complete with bacteria and viruses. The newspapers ran stories telling of babies being turned away due to lack of space, of the unit being a *tangle of equipment and oxygen cylinders*, the public *milling along the corridor outside the unit* and *doctors and nurses finding it impossible to move* in such a cramped space. One newspaper went on to say that: *The number of babies dying at birth or in the first week of life in Dr Barrie's unit is 12 per 1,000. The national average is 15 per 1,000. Dr Barrie says: 'If we had optimum conditions I believe we could achieve 8 per 1,000.'* Another paper ran a story about a baby who had died due to the inadequate conditions; my father attributed the delays to the hospital administrators.

In desperation, Dad approached the Variety Club, the wonderful children's charity, and they generously agreed to fund any expenses incurred by the move. This prompted managerial intransigence, administrators raising objections to the fact that money had been sought from a charity, management committees raising one objection after another. Dad was exasperated. Furthermore, he felt strongly that the reaction of the hospital to the magnificent offer from the Variety Club might be construed as downright ungrateful.

The wheels of NHS administration turn slowly. Eventually Dad's persistence paid off and on Friday 3rd July 1981 his neonatal unit opened at the West London Hospital. An opening ceremony was held, attended by the parents of premature babies, the local MP, and various dignitaries. Michael and Elizabeth Aspel, whose son Patrick had been treated in the unit, were the guests of honour. Dad made a speech in which he thanked the Variety Club of Great Britain.

The money had been raised by Applause, the 'young' arm of Variety Club, chaired by Linda Nissim. Their donation totalled £40,000, a huge sum in 1981, equivalent to around £200,000 today. The Young Variety Club's generosity allowed the move to go ahead, and furthermore paid for additional incubators. Linda Nissim addressed the crowd: 'Young Variety have the supreme satisfaction of knowing that through their efforts the lives of 150 babies will be saved every year.'

It was the most up-to-date, well-equipped and modern neonatal intensive care unit in London. Dad was justly proud. He now headed a neonatal unit of renown which accepted referrals from not just the local community, but also from other hospitals afar. Dad saw the need to further the success already borne out by his unit and others like it, and with the help of funds raised by the grateful parents of premature babies saved by his neonatal unit, he built a paediatric research laboratory. The hospital trustees gave him a small patch of land at the front of the hospital on which to construct this project, and his laboratory employed a full-time technician and carried out cutting-edge research into neonatal respiratory physiology and intensive care.

The new neonatal unit had provision to take babies not just from the maternity beds at the West London Hospital but from surrounding hospitals too. Nonetheless, Dad had worked out that statistically a premature baby's chances of survival were dramatically increased if it was born at Charing Cross Hospital. With the generous financial support of the Variety Club (again!), Dad developed a customised ambulance, complete with an incubator, resuscitation kit and a ventilator, that could bring premature babies direct to his unit. It was the first neonatal ambulance in the country (if not the world) and saved hundreds of young lives. Indeed, I have included in this book a warm and moving tribute from the mother of a baby whose life was saved by this vehicle. As my father later recalled: *the idea captured the imagination of countless generous people and before long, similar ambulances were donated to neonatal pioneers up and down the country, with even bigger and better vehicles in America, Germany and Japan. Soon I was working on Mark 2, followed by Mark 3. The whole story would fill a book.*

Dad was a keen and inspirational teacher. He would follow his juniors' careers with pride; they in turn remained devoted to him. Professor Hugh Pennington, the eminent microbiologist, recalls, 'Herbert Barrie was one of my most memorable medical teachers. I remember him as an ardent pioneer in the care of premature babies. When he started, success was so rare that after each [success] he gave his team champagne. He was a brilliant teacher and an exceptionally pleasant person'. Malcolm Levene, now emeritus professor of paediatrics and child health at the University of Leeds, was my father's senior house officer (SHO) in 1976, and then returned as registrar in 1978. He remembers Dad as 'convivial, charming and helpful. His was a fundamental contribution to the early status of neonatal medicine. He developed one of the first neonatal intensive care units in London.' He adds, however, that my father 'was not a team player. He didn't like to collaborate with others, but if he found someone who was enthusiastic about something he was very generous in acting as a mentor.'

Dr David Pyke was for many years the registrar of the Royal College of Physicians. He kept an amused eye on the funny, absurd, surprising and scandalous things he encountered; these he recorded in his regular column in the *College Commentary*. They were the most eagerly – often the *only* – items read by fellows of the college. David wished to thank my father for saving his granddaughter's life, and considered that it would be indiscreet to mention

Dad by name, more especially since my father had, as he put it, broken the law by saving an infant below the limit of viability.

In October 1983 Pyke wrote: *Although I am sure you cannot believe it I am old enough to be a grandfather, and am. But it wasn't all plain sailing. The girl was born at 26 weeks, so it was illegal, and having taken a bleary look at the world, dropped her weight to 780 grams. I thought this must be prohibitively light, but not so. Modern neonatal technology and modern neonatologists are both splendid and they kept this little bundle going with drips into an arm so small that it, let alone a vein, was hardly visible. I won't embarrass those who broke the law by converting this non-existent object into – as it happens – the most beautiful baby ever seen, but they make a point that can't be repeated too often – or rather two points; high-technology medicine can save lives, and lives that are worth saving, and it is not incompatible with treating a patient and family gently and considerately. The antithesis between curing and caring is false.*

A collection of these comments was published as *Pyke's Notes* (London, Royal College of Physicians, 1992).

Dr Stephen Hirst was my father's SHO in the 1970s. He remembers that 'Herbert Barrie was wonderful to ask for advice at any time. He was a true "organic" paediatrician. The juniors knew that if a child was really sick, really ill, Dr Barrie was the safest and wisest doctor to consult. His calm and ready help could treat a worried junior as well as the patient. Once in the early hours I rang him at home to say I could not get a ventilated premature baby to go pink. I had struggled with the ventilator without success. Before I knew it, there was Dr Barrie, smartly dressed in a shirt and tie with a clean white coat. Then, magic: a few adjustments by

Dr Barrie and the baby was a lovely colour. Oh joy! From Dr Barrie came a cheerful "How are the others doing?" Upon which he launched into a confidence-boosting, if tiring, ward round.'

Dad extolled the principles of medicine to generations of students, who eagerly attended his ward rounds, lectures and seminars. I remember that he would invite his students, and juniors too, back to our home for dinner. Stephen Hirst recalls, 'Dr Barrie invited me to his home for dinner. His wife was a doctor too, a microbiologist. I happened to mention to them that when I do any DIY I use a hand drill. 'Oh, that will never do.' Dr Barrie smiled, and then spent the next half an hour teaching me how to use a power drill. Years later I bumped into him and told him about a rare case of malignant pyrexia I had treated. He invited me back to his department to present the case to the students. How lucky I was to go on to practise within reach of his help and advice.'

My father would quietly delight in his juniors' subsequent careers. Witness to his influence is borne out by the number of young paediatricians coming from his department at Charing Cross Hospital.

Once on a family holiday to Rome, my father was smitten with a porcelain tondo hanging in the hotel bedroom. It was of the Virgin mother and child, and he was adamant that something like this should adorn the wall above the bank of incubators in his neonatal unit back in London. It was important, he said, for the mothers to know that love was very much a part of the unit's ethos, and for the junior doctors not to lose sight of humanity. The hotel manager was not, to Dad's dismay, prepared to sell the tondo, and so the family embarked on a search of the city for a pottery where one might be able to purchase such a thing. We struck lucky on the third day and returned to London, with not one but two beautiful glazed tondos – one being a spare in case of breakage!

With Jolly's retirement in 1983, my father became head of the department of child health. Now, as the physician in charge, he felt able to run the department with autonomy and it thrived as a centre of excellence at both an undergraduate and postgraduate level. As head of the department he was exacting about standards and accountability, was scrupulously fair, and had an instinctive grasp of right and wrong.

Dad was a man of disarming simplicity in whom social decorum blended indistinguishably into gentleness and humility. He was a champion of the weak and the poor and showed considerable obstinacy in furthering their cause both publicly and in smaller ways in his work. His clientele, if that's the right word, ranged from residents of the local Peabody estates to parents drawn from the worlds of politics and the arts.

His patients received his unremitting care and were loyal to him: many parents became personal friends for life. He was a person who genuinely seemed to like everyone that he met (NHS bureaucrats and most social workers excepted!). He always looked for the best in people and he invariably found it – even when others might have questioned whether that person even *had* any goodness! I would add that he was compassionate, kind to children and their parents alike, and a sensitive, cultured man. But he also had perspicacity and tenacity. Certainly his resolve to ensure the survival of babies long before their usual gestation, his fight to ensure that his vision for his neonatal unit was realised, and his drive at work are testimony to his stalwart determination. Sometimes this came across as stubbornness.

In this book I have collated much of my father's written work. Although Dad's scientific articles were, in effect, his legacy, especially in terms of resuscitation of the newborn infant, I have deliberately omitted these. Instead I have chosen a selection of his writings on other topics. Most of these are connected with, and relate to, his career in medicine. A not insignificant number pertain directly to paediatric practice. All the footnotes in the pages that follow are my own.

I have generally placed the pieces in chronological order. The exceptions are Dad's contributions to *The Lancet* In England Now columns. Here the journal published the musings of peripatetic correspondents, the essential ingredients being wit, wisdom and humanity. The editor of *The Lancet* at that time was Theodore Fox (later Sir Theodore): and he and Dad got on very well. Indeed, TF, as he was known, would invite Dad to join him for lunch at his club. It was at such a lunch that he asked Dad whether he would like to join *The Lancet* as a deputy editor. It was presumed – although not spoken aloud – that upon TF's retirement Dad would become editor. Dad considered this invitation but paediatrics meant the world to him, and after some deliberation he declined. Thank goodness! The years that followed were my father's most productive; the pioneering work on neonatal resuscitation was all still to come.

And yet my father was unpretentious and diffident about his achievements: *Now pushing ninety and long past my sell-by date, I became medieval history at Charing Cross Hospital the day I left. But for a few dedicated anthropologists and parties of bored schoolchildren, dinosaurs would have been long forgotten too.*

I hope my father would have liked this book. He

possessed virtues of wisdom, restraint and discernment, but he could also be reticent with his feelings, almost aloof, and even with his family he could be reserved. But Dad often said that one day he would bring all his articles together into a published collection.

Dad – this is your story in your own words.

Michael Barrie
March 2018

Chapter One

Tributes from Friends
and Colleagues

Elizabeth Aspel
Mother of Patrick

I met Dr Herbert Barrie in 1980 when my son Patrick was born at twenty-eight weeks. I had gone into labour far too early, and I was in St Teresa's Hospital in Wimbledon. Fortunately the specially equipped ambulance was summoned from Charing Cross Hospital as soon as I went into labour, so that when Patrick was born he received life-saving treatment straightaway. He was taken immediately to the special care baby unit and into the arms of Dr Barrie and his team. I discovered later that this ambulance was entirely his brainchild, and the precious extra minutes it gave to the premature babies was a great factor in increasing their chances of survival. A Charing Cross Hospital on wheels!

It is impossible to exaggerate the anxiety and fear

experienced by a parent when their child's life hangs in the balance from day to day. There are so many things that can go wrong. Yet Dr Barrie had the most wonderfully calm and reassuring manner that gave one the courage to face each hurdle. It struck me afterwards that given what a compassionate man he was, it was rather unfortunate that the only reason one would ever have cause to get to know him was under the most frightening circumstances. Not that he seemed to mind that at all; he clearly loved his work and was determined that all his babies would get the best possible start in life. He did regard them all as an extended family and we were urged to return every year for the Christmas party on his unit, so that he could see how all of them were getting on.

I suppose all consultants must cultivate that quality of detachment which enables them to make difficult decisions about vulnerable patients without it taking too much out of them emotionally. They could not do their job otherwise. But I doubt there are too many who give parents their home phone number with the instruction to 'ring at any time'; an invitation that I took full advantage of.

My son is now thirty-seven years old and is in rude good health. Thank you, Herbert, from both of us.

Lesley Agutter
Mother of Rupert

With Rupert's birth in 1972 our lives changed dramatically. Our son's disabilities meant a different future than we might have expected, but crucially they also meant that Dr Herbert Barrie entered our lives; he cared so wonderfully for Rupert over the following months as an inpatient in Charing Cross Hospital, and also for us as we struggled to come to terms with an unknown future. Herbert Barrie's compassion and warm humanity meant that he felt our anxieties as keenly as we did and he did all he could to help us, including allowing us to bring Rupert home for a few hours having first taught me (with no prior nursing background) to pass a nasogastric tube from Rupert's nose into his small stomach; a necessary lesson because Rupert kept pulling it out! This meant that for a short while we could experience the reality of being new parents, which meant so much to us both.

Herbert (I use his first name because over the years that followed we became friends) was an inspirational paediatrician but above all such a kind and caring doctor to his patients and their families, which meant that at the very lowest point of one's life one never felt alone.

My husband and I will always be indebted to him for all that he did for us during Rupert's early years. We feel truly blessed to have known such a great man and to have benefited from his skill and friendship.

Dr Peter Husband
Consultant Paediatrician (Retired), London, England

Dr Herbert Barrie was by far the most important person to help me in my career. It was his teaching at St Thomas's Hospital which first made me think of a profession in paediatrics, and I was then subsequently lucky and privileged to be his registrar, and then senior registrar, at Charing Cross Hospital. I admired him not only for his high intellectual and neonatal prowess, but also for his humble nature. Indeed, he was a kind and gentle person and a wonderful role model for a young paediatrician such as myself.

I regarded Herbert as my 'paediatric father' yet his kindness extended beyond that: I had two difficult family problems when I worked for him, and Herbert was of course the one I turned to for support. Naturally he provided solace and guidance, and this made a great difference to my life.

His wife Dinah, his daughter Caroline, and his son Michael are much in my thoughts and prayers; and I personally lament the loss of such a wonderful man.

Joe Ruston
Fellow Tennis Player

Herbert was a keen tennis player. He joined Coombe Wood Tennis Club in 1970 and the sports club at King's College School in 1999.

I suppose that I first played with him at King's in 2007 as he approached the age of eighty. He was then a nimble player but as he became less mobile he established himself in a commanding position at the net – earning from us the Germanic moniker *Der Netmeister*. It was very hard to get a ball past Herbert, but as our fellow tennis player Nick Goddard remarked, 'When your beautifully crafted passing shot was intercepted and expertly put away, the enigmatic smile that spread over Herbert's face was ample compensation for a point lost.'

At Coombe Wood, Herbert enjoyed the open sessions on Thursdays and Sundays when anyone could turn up and play. One day, he noticed a small boy watching from the side of the court and invited him to join in. That seven-year-old boy was Ollie Lloyd, who is now the head coach at the club. Ollie still treasures that act of kindness.

Herbert had an amusing way of describing the various ailments that interfered with his tennis, and he enjoyed corresponding by email. This week I read through some of those messages: they are pithy and funny. Here's one from the day after we had played in March 2011: *Most of it was not great today. I didn't serve particularly well, I didn't move well and I didn't hit a lot of winners.* It turned out that those were not Herbert's own words but, as he teasingly went on to reveal, those of Andy Murray!

In 2012 Herbert gave up his membership at King's so

I – and other friends who missed his presence on the court or in the pub afterwards – began visiting him at his home in Burghley Avenue. Here is a typical example of an email invitation from Herbert: *As they say in Abu Dhabi when the air conditioning isn't working – a warm welcome always awaits you here.*

One of the themes of tea with Herbert was his eclectic choice of edible treats. In addition to delicious smoked salmon sandwiches, he took pleasure in serving pastries with foreign – and sometimes rather saucy – names. We enjoyed Viennese whirls, Italian panettone, and a host of others, but his special favourite was French fancies. When I say we, I mean Dinah and me because Herbert himself hardly ate a thing. He was content to enjoy the pleasure of others.

Herbert was loyal and kind to his friends. When Nick Goddard tore a muscle, Herbert was the first to offer to drive him home. When Bill Culver was in St Mary's Hospital, Herbert masterminded a Colditz-style escape in a laundry basket so that Bill could enjoy a barbecue with the Goddards and the rest of the tennis team. When a friend, Siân, was unwell, he offered to drive round at a moment's notice should she need any help. The thought of Herbert at almost ninety, steaming down Roehampton Lane with a flashing blue light on his car, was as amusing as it was typical of the man.

Friends of Herbert will know that he loved music and that he played the violin, but imagine him giving a perfect rendering of *Happy Birthday* after dinner in Burghley Avenue just a few years ago. Another happy memory for those of us who heard it.

The last time I had tea with Herbert and Dinah we started talking about plastic bags and the clear warning printed on them: *This is not a toy*. I suggested that few modern kids would be very happy with the gift of an empty plastic bag, but this triggered an immediate response in Herbert. He led me up to his office and pulled down an article that he had written in 1971 for *The Lancet* explaining a new treatment for babies with respiratory problems. This was CPAP – continuous positive airway pressure. Herbert's invention – which was as simple and economical as it was groundbreaking – involved a plastic bag which he popped over the infant's head and inflated to a controlled pressure. It was wonderful to hear him explain this procedure with such clarity and enthusiasm.

In November 2013 I wrote to Herbert saying that it had been nice to see him and Dinah at the funeral of Bill Culver, the captain of our little tennis group at King's. In his reply, Herbert included a line from Walt Whitman; words that might apply to a different captain and a much-valued friend: *O Captain! My Captain! Our fearful trip is done.*

Jan Gifford
Scientist, Adventurer and Samaritan

Dr Herbert Barrie made a big impact on me when I first arrived in England and started work at St Thomas's Hospital, and his friendship was something very special to me.

Herbert was the leading light behind all the work on blood gases in premature babies. I found the work interesting and stimulating, and Herbert included me in all the discussions. It was trailblazing stuff and I was thrilled to play a very small part in it. Herbert was interested in the activities of all us young Kiwis who travelled right across the world for the big adventure in Britain.

He was a very special man – gentlemanly, sincere, deep-thinking, with wide interests and a lovely sense of humour. He had an important influence on my life and for that I will always be grateful.[1]

---

1. It is with sadness that I report that Jan passed away just a few weeks after sending this tribute to me. I send my condolences to her three sons, Duncan, Andrew and Hugh.

Jean Hendy-Harris
Author and Mother of Patrick

Patrick was born in 1968 at Charing Cross Hospital at twenty-eight weeks' gestation. He was very, very small. That kind of prematurity is not a big deal these days but back then it certainly was. Patrick could not have had better care. Dr Herbert Barrie was a very significant figure in our lives and went to extraordinary lengths to ensure life became a little easier for Patrick and me.

When Patrick was six months old, Dr Barrie told me I would be able to take him home from hospital within a week or so. I was over the moon, but my excitement was dashed when I received a letter from the hospital's social worker (a Miss Hinton, I think). She wrote that although I had been informed by Dr Barrie that I could bring my baby home, before this would be possible a social worker would have to visit my home (then a basement flat in Paddington) in order to 'inspect' it to ensure that it was a suitable environment for a baby. I was absolutely incensed: I went directly to the hospital in order to uplift Patrick, as I presumed they would not actually be keeping him under lock and key in the interim. My anger revolved entirely around the fact that had I been married I would not have been sent such a letter.

When I tried to take my baby from his cot, security was called. They in turn alerted Miss Hinton, who did her best to stop me, getting increasingly distressed and breathless (I think she suffered from asthma). Within minutes a 'scene' had developed and there was chaos and much shouting. And then Dr Barrie arrived. He calmed everyone down and told me – in front of Miss Hinton and the security team – that I could take Patrick home immediately. Within minutes of Dr

Barrie arriving things were back on an even keel, although Miss Hinton was most put out.

A couple of years later I happened to notice some disparaging comments in Patrick's notes regarding the *socially unacceptable part-time work* I was involved in at the time. Dr Barrie ordered that the notes be rewritten so that the remarks would not follow Patrick around. He even sent me a copy of the updated record.

Dr Barrie never lectured me about the choices I was making. He found me part-time work as a typist for a paediatrician[2] in Harley Street, who in turn passed me on to type for his brother, a dermatologist. I invested in a medical dictionary as not being able to spell words like 'psoriasis' was a stumbling block!

But Dr Barrie did not stop there. He was solely responsible for ensuring that my first articles were published in various magazines. This in turn led to my short stories appearing in print, and this ultimately led to various books.

Herbert Barrie also worked hard to ensure that I made the momentous decision to marry Hank and move to New Zealand. Dr Barrie was always right and his gut feelings were invariably the correct ones. If it was not for his influence and persistence I would not be the person I am today.

He was quite unlike the medical specialists at the time who seemed only too aware of their own importance and position, and who were overly concerned as to how the world viewed them, following fads and fancies if they thought they would add to their overall esteem. Dr Barrie was the complete opposite. His enormous strengths were his humanity and the way in which he was able to care for children and their families, seeing them as people rather

---

2.   Dr Alfred White Franklin (1905 – 1984), consultant paediatrician and one-time president of the British Paediatric Association.

than 'cases'. This is of course why he was loved and trusted so much, and why he will not easily be forgotten. He cared for his patients, but also enriched the lives of their families. I will miss him and I will never forget him.

I told Patrick that Dr Herbert Barrie had died. 'Ah,' he said, 'the violin-playing paediatrician.' Which of course he was.

Angela Bennett MD
Professor of Pediatrics (Retired),
Downstate Medical Center,
New York

I first met Herbert Barrie in 1976 at Downstate Medical Center, Brooklyn. Dr Dav Cook, a friend of Herbert's from the years they had spent in Boston as young researchers, was at that time chairman of the department of pediatrics, and he invited Herbert to spend a month in New York as visiting professor. It was a most memorable month for everyone on the faculty; all of us learned so much from Herbert's excellent teaching, from his impressive fund of knowledge and clinical insights, and from observing the kind and gentle example he set in his practice of the profession. He was a wonderful doctor. All the pediatricians at Downstate grew to love and respect him, and we were upset to see him leave at the end of the month.

It was my good fortune to be told by Dav Cook to make sure that Herbert was, to use his words, 'well taken care of'. I was delighted to oblige – and promptly arranged for some sightseeing excursions, for outings to my home with my husband Jack, and for dinner at various New York restaurants. One such dinner date was interrupted by a call with the news that our son John, a college student at Columbia University, had been admitted to hospital with suspected appendicitis.

'Well, of course we must go to examine him ourselves,' said Herbert with authority, and off we went to do so.

My brother Ed, also a doctor, was already at the hospital when we arrived so John had the benefit of three consultants to diagnose what was indeed a case of acute appendicitis.

The patient went to surgery and had an uneventful recovery.

In another funny story, Herbert was surprised and rather shocked when a group of diners at an elegant New York restaurant began singing a loud rendition of *Happy Birthday* for one of the guests at their table. Herbert said that he had never seen anything like that done in London. He must have had second thoughts about it because he told me some time later that he had caused quite a stir in a local restaurant when he introduced the practice for his wife Dinah's birthday. I would love to have been there to witness this breach of traditional British decorum!

I kept in touch with Herbert after he returned home to England. He and Dinah visited us when they came to the United States for a short vacation in the 1990s, and I visited him some years later when my husband and I went to England on holiday. Brief as these encounters may seem, they were nonetheless meaningful enough to cement what became a long and enduring friendship. And through the years we kept in touch with greetings, letters and emails. I will greatly miss that friendship. Herbert was indeed a very special man.

Dr Bashir Qureshi
General Practitioner and Author of 'Transcultural Medicine'

It is a fact that from the time one is born until the moment of death, one does nothing but fill time. However, some people care for the human race tirelessly throughout their life: Dr Herbert Barrie was one such person. Over his long life he has left an enormous legacy of better care for all babies from different backgrounds worldwide. When he returned from Boston, USA, after his research fellowship work at the Children's Medical Center in the 1950s, he pioneered the idea of sliding a plastic tube into an anoxic neonate's lungs to provide oxygen, an innovation which has saved many premature babies' lives. Herbert was a consultant paediatrician at Charing Cross Hospital in London from 1965 to 1986 and spent all his life in learning, teaching, examining, and serving children and their carers. He helped many charities as well.

I met Dr Herbert Barrie in 1981 when I spent two weeks training in a clinical attachment at the paediatric department at Charing Cross Hospital. I was then a GP and a clinical medical officer in paediatrics. I have long felt that there exists an aura: one likes some people straight away and others one dislikes. I liked Herbert from the outset – and we kept in touch until he passed away in 2017.

When I was working in his department at Charing Cross Hospital I recollect that Herbert was a tall, calm and well-dressed man with a calculated way of thinking. He cared for children and their parents equally. I remember that in the outpatients' clinic he sat behind his desk, with the mother and her child seated on his right side. I would be sat, observing, on the left side of the table. No one would sit on the opposite side of the desk: Herbert thought that far too formal. He would let the mother or father talk as long as they wished, and he would then examine the child very thoroughly. He was emotionally close to the parents. Each consultation was superb.

Dr Herbert Barrie's outpatient session was held in the morning. After he had finished, another consultant paediatrician[3] would arrive and do the afternoon outpatients session. The nurses had to quickly move the furniture around because this other consultant insisted on the old-fashioned arrangement where the parent and child sit opposite the doctor, with the table in between them. This second paediatrician had a public-school accent (and manner!); he had worked in Africa and adopted a pleasant, colonial attitude. He was not emotionally attached to parents and assumed a 'ruler and subject' approach, albeit with a sympathetic attitude.

Interestingly, these two paediatricians did not see eye to eye,[4] but I looked into the eyes of both of them. I was aware that 'looking in the eye' is essential in England, but it is very rude in Asian and African countries. I had to change, and I did exactly that!

When I was the editor of *Faculty News*, the newsletter of the local faculty of the Royal College of General

---

3.   Dr Hugh Jolly.

4.   Dr Stephen Hirst recalled an interesting anecdote. Hugh Jolly always drove an expensive sports car. One day there was a loud bang in the middle of the night; his car had quite literally exploded, causing considerable damage to the house. Stephen recalls sitting in the paediatric outpatient clinic with Jolly when there was a knock on the door. My father popped his head round. 'Hugh, I'm sorry to hear about your car. Look – we live close to each other. Let me drive you home this evening, and I can give you a lift every day until you sort things out.'

Practitioners, in the 1980s, Herbert was one of my favourite writers. Whenever I want to speak, I first assess three things: a) Have I got something new to say? b) Is there anyone willing to listen? c) For how long should I speak? I noticed that Dr Herbert Barrie sought to fulfil the same criteria. This link made me trust him and thus invite him to write several guest editorials. His concise pieces were always informative, educational, thought-provoking and sometimes controversial. We all know that criticism in small doses is a positive thinking in science and politics.

Herbert loved his wife Dinah, his son Michael and his daughter Caroline. He used not to have a television at home so that Michael and Caroline would spend time studying after school and not get carried away by watching children's programmes on television. Once he winked and told me that they slipped out to watch television at a neighbour's house!

Dr Herbert Barrie seconded my nomination for the FRCPCH (Fellow of the Royal College of Paediatrics and Child Health). We used to meet each other at college events and compare notes. I will miss him always, but the memories are forever.

Sally Vinter
Mother of Susie

Dr Herbert Barrie was very important to us in the first few weeks and months of our daughter's life. Susie was born at the West London Hospital[5] in early 1985. She had an atrioventricular septal defect[6] and Down's syndrome. We were told that she was unlikely to survive. I have a back problem and thus had a difficult pregnancy with pain in my spine. Understandably, my husband wondered if he could cope both with a wife with difficulties and a baby with significant challenges. Added to which, my mother and my husband's mother were of a background and generation who felt that it would be better all-round if we left the baby in the hospital.

My husband wanted to explore the options. Dr Barrie made himself available to us and gave us a great deal of time over the next few weeks. We would meet with him in his office at Charing Cross Hospital and he would go through the various possibilities. None of them seemed acceptable to me, and at about the three-week stage I knew that if the baby and I were not wanted then we would somehow manage on our own. Dr Barrie patiently explored our concerns and never once put pressure on us to make up our minds. He maintained that Susie was a strong little thing and unlike some of his colleagues he refused to be pessimistic about her future. He showed me her strength by putting his fingers gently across her nose; she struggled

---

5. The maternity department and special care baby unit of Charing Cross Hospital were based at the nearby West London Hospital.

6. Atrioventricular septal defect is the most common congenital heart defect found in children with Down's syndrome.

to get his fingers away and catch her breath. Dr Barrie was right! She was a strong little thing.

Dr Barrie said that my husband would come round and that he would become proud of her, rather as one might be proud of a particularly fine car. (This made me smile as my husband had never been remotely interested in cars!)

At five weeks we brought Susie home and never looked back. My husband became – and still is – the most wonderful father to her. I am convinced that it was Dr Barrie's steady, patient, non-pressurising and non-judgemental help that made this possible for us. Alas, I doubt very much that new parents today get that degree of support. He also arranged for us to be registered with the best GP in the area.[7]

At the time, I wondered how I would manage on my own looking after a baby with so many difficulties. How would I know if she were seriously ill? 'You'll just know,' said Dr Barrie. He was right. Within just a few hours you have a benchmark of what is normal for your child.

After several months of 'advice' from other parents, and organisations both here and abroad, I remember asking Dr Barrie if I should be giving her extra oxygen or taking her abroad for intensive physiotherapy.

'No,' he replied. 'Just enjoy her.' On one occasion he told me Susie had a face like a potato. I bridled a bit but he was right, and in any case it was meant affectionately!

For several years after Susie was born, I was asked to give talks to midwives, health visitors and nurses on what it was like to have a handicapped baby. I would always pay tribute to Dr Barrie; I would emphasise the importance of giving people time and space to adjust to difficult situations, just as he had given me.

Dr Barrie played such an important part in our lives

---

7. Dr Stephen Hirst.

thirty-two years ago. He really did make a difference. Susie is now a happy, well-adjusted adult. She is a member of a dance company[8] which travels all over the world. She also helps out in the nursery of a local primary school. She has heard over the years about the doctor who looked after her when she was a baby, and she was sad when I told her the news of his passing. A few months ago, Susie developed a painful rash on her legs. She said to me mournfully, 'I wish Dr Barrie was here. He'd know what to do.' Of course she couldn't really remember him properly, but his name lives on in the family!

8. The Larondina Dance Company. This is in demand at home and abroad, with performances in Russia, France, Hungary and Ecuador. In 2013 the company (competing under the name of 'Dance For Joy') reached the semi-finals of a Sky TV dance competition.

Anne Barker
Mother of Camilla, Davina, Edwina and Felicity

Herbert Barrie was the paediatrician who checked our first daughter. He also had to tell us that our second daughter had Down's syndrome. He did it incrementally, gently, and with immense sensitivity.

The duty paediatrician who attended our third daughter, born weeks after her Down's sister had died, was brusque when I sought reassurance that this baby really was all right. Sister got rid of him, rang Dr Barrie, and he came in from home immediately. He went over the infant from top to toe, showing me she was absolutely fine. He left instructions that if I had another child, he was to be called.

Dr Barrie was the perfect meld of culture, warmth, professionalism, humanity and excellent doctoring. He put his tiny patients first, but on all occasions he ranked their mother alongside them in a model demonstration of emotional intelligence and pure kindness.

Chapter Two

In His Own Words: Writings, Articles and Musings by Dr Herbert Barrie

In England Now
A Running Commentary by Peripatetic Correspondents

When Bertie the Burglar was X-rayed for swallowed valuables and found to have tuberculosis as well, he was transferred to our hospital. His arrival made quite a stir in the reception office before we had completed his admission form. The diverse items, ranging from *Religion* to *Consent for Post Mortem*, were all filled in, but the space headed *Occupation* still showed a conspicuous blank, and a protracted argument ensued.

All were agreed that to enter 'burglar' was to prejudice the likelihood of reform. Likewise 'prisoner', 'convict', or 'jailbird' denoted pessimism in the corrective possibilities of our penal system. Nondescript terms such as 'labourer' or 'odd-job man' were discarded so as to avoid undesirable litigation with the appropriate unions. 'Unemployed' seemed likely to cause later difficulty over unemployment benefit; nor could anyone who was serving a sentence be truly described as 'out of work'. Inspiration came from our junior clerk who suggested 'bugler' (deliberate mistake like they do on the television, see?), but the general reaction was that any misspelling of the word was dangerous and liable to abuse. Suggestions that 'income-tax inspector', 'garage proprietor' and 'barrow-boy' were all synonyms for 'robber' were dismissed. In view of determined opposition from the occupational therapist, 'stonemason' and 'mailbag manufacturer' were also abandoned. The compromise finally agreed upon was 'self-employed'.

The Lancet, March 1954

* * * *

At our staff meeting last week a consultant complained bitterly that much of his work could be done at registrar level. His remark is not unjustified; but raises the fresh difficulty of defining the upper limits of the houseman's lowliness and the lower limits of the consultant's elevation.

For instance, the level of the surgical registrar, with his tail-end operating-lists for haemorrhoids and hernia, lies on a distinctly inguino-perineal plane, while that of his orthopaedic colleague is governed by centrifugal force, for his endeavours are confined almost exclusively to the big toe or the little finger. In the ENT terrain the pillars of the fauces[1] form convenient landmarks, golden gates beyond which a registrar rarely trespasses.

In gynaecology and anaesthetics the level is not so much a matter of height as of depth, varying in direct proportion

---

1.   The arched opening at the back of the mouth.

to seniority in gynaecology and inverse proportion in anaesthetics. Classification of the psychiatric registrar is not feasible, for one can never be certain whether his level lies above or below the id.

What about the medical registrar? Why, I see all the patients over ninety.

The Lancet, April 1954

* * * *

Why do ward sisters delight in transposing all the beds like a shuffled pack of cards? In the good old days it was enough for beds to be in geometrically straight lines with bed tables and lockers at right angles, wheels retracted through 180 degrees, and flowers trimmed to a uniform height. Thus they remained, apart from placing the garrulous near the door with deaf or non-English-speaking neighbours. Now, however, patients have become pieces of furniture – to be rubbed, dusted and moved around the ward. I believe this is all part of an organised conspiracy to undermine our conditioned reflexes – a mischievous plot to throw the ranks of the medical profession into Pavlovian confusion. No sooner do I begin to recognise Mrs A in the third bed, with obesity and chronic bronchitis, than she is replaced by Mrs B who has ulcerated legs but bears a striking resemblance to her predecessor. Any fresh acquaintance is doomed to short life because there is always a Mrs C with gall bladder trouble and like ample features to add to the confusion, and there are times when I suspect I have seen the same patient twice on one round. Then, adding insult to injury, the house-physician is blamed for getting the notes out of order.

The Lancet, June 1954

* * * *

Derby Day always brings its little store of excitement, but our proximity to the racecourse is a doubtful asset. True, all clinics are cancelled, but not with the idea of letting us go to watch the fun. At all other times competition for outpatient appointments is fierce, but on this one day of the year the local inhabitants have no wish to see a specialist. On the other hand the casualty officer is usually provided with reinforcements, and empty beds are kept ready for Pott's fractures, perforated peptic ulcers, and cerebral haemorrhages, which are the chief sporting risks of the turf. Attacks of paranoid hysteria ('I've been robbed!') are not infrequent, and there is said to be a significant increase in the incidence of pediculosis.[2] Complications among inpatients are few, but the house-surgeon always goes round the chronic blocks after the commentary, reducing herniae.

Our first admission was a schoolteacher from the Midlands who, in the heat of the final furlong, had a rigor. 'And what might a Birmingham schoolmaster be doing on Epsom Downs on a Wednesday afternoon?' we asked. 'Brushing up his arithmetic, of course,' came the reply; then, as a glum afterthought: 'Subtraction sums.'

But on the whole this was a satisfactory year. Few patients, merry or moribund, could resist backing Never Say Die, and even a confused old granny, who has entertained suicidal notions for years, insisted on two shillings each way.

The Lancet, June 1954

---

2.   Scabies.

* * * *

My holiday intention this year was to forget all about medicine. So I travelled to a foreign land where I hoped that a strange language and strange customs would protect me from my profession. But I had scarcely arrived when my colleagues sought me out, and before long we were clustered together in a little clinical conference. The symposium consisted of a general practitioner from Holland, whose chief assets were the sound common sense he brought from his country practice and the diverting vivaciousness and charm of his two daughters; a chest physician from Alsace with whose wisdom I could barely keep pace, though I became expert in flipping the pages of my dictionary; and a gynaecologist from Belgium, who, for obvious reasons, found himself at a diagnostic disadvantage.

We regarded ourselves as well equipped to discuss the clinical aspects of our fellow guests. The affectionate little girl with protruding tongue and pink eyelids, we all agreed, had Down's syndrome. The head waiter probably had alcoholic cirrhosis, but he was a nice chap and we unanimously accorded him a good prognosis. The old fat lady, who shuffled about painfully with two sticks, proved more difficult. Rheumatoid arthritis seemed likely, but she always sat outside, in sunshine or rain. The suggestion that she might be the surgical success of a pinned fractured femur was applauded. The slate-blue discoloration of the face of the gentleman dining in the corner aroused lively interest. I was in favour of sulphaemoglobinaemia – mercifully almost the same word exists in French and Dutch. The fact that the colour seemed less pronounced on the day after we had spinach for dinner was held not to be without significance. The Dutch doctor had little support for his diagnosis of argyria,[3] but, unlike the rest of us, he had seen a case. Even psychiatric problems came up for our consideration, and we all agreed that the exuberant gentleman who went for a swim at 6am each morning, and played ferocious ping-pong after every meal, could take a thrice-daily dose of phenobarbitone with advantage.

We also enjoyed discussing natural conditions of work and exchanging nomenclature. I was interested to hear that the Continental physician is called a specialist of internal diseases, and my colleagues were astounded to learn that, under our beneficent health service, most of the patients I now see have no disease, external or internal.

The Lancet, July 1954

* * * *

Of all musical instruments, few have the evil potential of the violin, for what can be more distressing to the tortured ear than the misappropriation of horsehair to catgut? Perhaps that is why it appears so frequently in pharmaceutical advertisements. One, for instance, shows the instrument beneath the caption 'In Labour' to stress the advantages, if not the dire necessity, of anaesthesia. As a physician dedicated to the relief of suffering, I play rarely now, and then only to enliven some spirit-fuelled party with a realistic rendition of *The Little Red Monkey* or the gregarious strains of *The Whiffenpoof Song*. But occasionally a working knowledge of the fiddle proves useful as in the case of Madelaine.

Madelaine complained of pain in her right shoulder.

---

3. Excessive exposure to silver. The most dramatic symptom of argyria is that the skin turns a purple or blue/grey colour.

A passionate devotee of the violin, she spent all her spare time practising the works of the great masters until the pain affected her playing, despite physiotherapy and the liniments and lotions her doctor could muster. Rest gave her relief but this was not a sacrifice she was prepared to make. Unlike the average teenager of today, she spoke of Bach and Beethoven with reverence. Their compositions, abounding in formidable fugues and arpeggios, are enough to strain the stoutest spinati, where indeed her symptoms lay.

Both to her and her GP my advice must have seemed strange. Henceforth, she was to apply herself to the altogether more gentle sonatas of Haydn and the legato divertimenti of Mozart. A little Handel and Schubert were allowed once a week and the bowing études of Corelli were banned altogether.

I never saw Madelaine again, but a short paragraph in a local paper caught my eye. She was praised for a polished performance. Her entire programme consisted of works by Bach and her recital was on the harpsichord.

The Lancet, August 1954

* * * *

To hear us talk, anyone might think that we live on the treacherous slopes of some mountain where the inhabitants, like Sisyphus' stone, are doomed to descend the well-worn path to the lower world. Gravity-conscious GPs continually 'phone up and say: 'Poor old so-and-so is slowly going downhill.' Some two or three weeks later we are forced to write back regretfully: 'Poor old so-and-so rapidly went downhill.' And to our pathologist, who is continually making unreasonable demands on our clinical acumen, we confide that poor old so-and-so went downhill, slowly at first but rapidly after coming into hospital.

No wonder I have nightmares. I dream of a long, straight road whose gentle incline disappears into a dim red haze in the distance. It is a one-way street and the pavement on both sides is crowded with pedestrians – all plodding downhill in a slow, steady stream. Only the hospital patients move fast; …they are provided with free transport.

The Lancet, September 1954

* * * *

Science at school is flourishing, my old chemistry master tells me. The biologists appear to be particularly enterprising. One of the senior boys has taken up bee-keeping in a big way and since he alone in this district has the skill and fortitude to deal with a swarm, he now proudly displays some half a dozen hives in the school playground. The experiment has proved a great success except for the disquieting thought that it may come to a prematurely sticky end if the headmaster were to get stung.

Another praiseworthy innovation is the biological pond. Unfortunately, the would-be engineers of the sixth form chose the wrong kind of cement and nothing will grow in it because the water will persist in being too alkaline. The bottom has been scrubbed soundly with brooms and slave labour, but the only result the biologists were able to report was the continued absence of water algae and an increased morbidity among the few surviving tadpoles. The chemistry department has not unnaturally displayed great interest in the problem, and after much ceremony, a measured quantity of concentrated nitric acid was stirred in. There was much bubbling of CO_2 for some days but, at last, samples of the water yielded pure cultures of anaerobic organisms. The matter has stimulated frantic research and great things are expected of one young scholar who is experimenting with a new buffer. Meanwhile, someone has bubbled in oxygen and eliminated even the anaerobes.

The Lancet, September 1954

* * * *

Now that the Motor Show is here again, I am seized afresh with the urge to reform the industry. All garages would be taken over by regional boards, management committees, and executive councils, and a comprehensive National Motor Service would provide free treatment to all ailing British automobiles – and possibly foreign ones as well. The service would be staffed by highly trained practitioners, required to serve a statutory period of apprenticeship in a teaching garage and to pass a written, oral, and practical qualifying examination. New appointments would be made by selection committees from some thirty or forty applicants, so as to promote healthy competition.

At the garage, all vehicles would have a searching history elicited, including past breakdowns, housing conditions, and the state of the waterworks and exhaust. Examination will follow the usual routine of inspection, palpation, and auscultation of the various systems. After a careful check from bonnet to boot, all positive and negative findings will be recorded. Where necessary, specimens will be sent to the laboratory for estimation of the radiator rust or the carburettor carbon expressed in milli-equivalents per litre.

Treatment will be under the direction of a physician or technician. The former, ably versed in conservative therapy, will probably prescribe potent mixtures to be poured into the radiator or down the petrol tank three times daily after runs. When a cure is not possible, the car will be referred to the technician for structural alteration, which may vary from a minor anastomosis of the brake cable to a major resection of the big end.

Ethics are strict and breaches of professional secrecy, negligence or dishonesty are punishable by erasure from the register. Unfortunately, it has become fashionable to recognise professional integrity by abuse, and, such is the litigiousness of the average public, membership of a Motor Defence Union would have to be compulsory.

The Lancet, October 1954

* * * *

Reviews in this journal are unsigned; but the honour of introducing a work of outstanding greatness comes but rarely, and it is not fitting that so great a privilege should pass shrouded in anonymity. *The Lancet* is therefore making an exception to this tradition for its review of Professor Herzschmerz's recently published *Einführung in die Elektrokardiographie.*

The title of this work is unpretentious, for it consists of 14 volumes, comprises some 15,000 pages and contains over 27,139 references. Volume 1 deals with the configuration of the P wave, and the first seven chapters are devoted to its absence. Each subsequent volume describes a part of the complex in some detail, and the author is to be congratulated on his masterly division of the QRS complex into its three components. Volumes 12, 13, and 14 are wisely set aside for a very comprehensive index and list of references.

The author succeeds admirably in his aim to remove prejudice against the use of exploring electrodes introduced directly into the ventricle through the intercostal spaces. There is a fascinating account of the use of umbilical leads in neonates, and a chapter on the electrocardiogram of the dachshund is an interesting novelty. There are a few minor points of criticism although these need in no way detract from the general high standard. On page 853, line 4, the word potassium is misspelt 'potasium', and the illustration of dextrocardia is unfortunately printed upside down. The effect of uranium on the U wave is dismissed in eleven pages, whereas a whole chapter is given to calcium lack. The recent work of Knicker, Smith, and Bocker on *Triaxial Vector Gradients* will no doubt be included in a subsequent edition. The colour of the cover is in pleasing harmony with the shade of the wrapping, but the weight of the volumes makes reading tiring on the arms.

These 14 volumes represent everything which the cardiologist, the consulting physician, the physiologist, the postgraduate, the experimental worker, and the medical student need to know about the subject, and form an invaluable work of reference for general practitioners and technicians. It seems almost too much to hope for an English translation soon, in order to widen still further its field of usefulness.

The Lancet, December 1954

* * * *

Life in most hospitals passes quietly, and any minor departure from routine, such as the ejection of the residents' piano from an upstairs window, is liable to hit newspaper headlines. Our latest claim to fame began with Night Sister's discovery of an unwanted man in the sluice. For reasons still not quite clear, the resident obstetric officer was summoned to deal with her attendant vasomotor phenomena,[4] and, since resident obstetricians tend to spring from a small-statured race, our colleague saw fit to bear a long stretcher-pole under his arm for protection. Meanwhile the intruder had vanished without trace and the police decided to bring their bloodhound into action. A large, sad-faced animal called Pluto was duly brought to the scene of the incident; but, overwhelmed by a host of new smells, he shook himself violently, chased his tail a few times, and made off in the direction of the labour ward where he barked loudly at a placenta lying in a bowl. The commotion woke the babies in the nursery, who all started yelling at once. Pluto took to instant flight and, after a careful search, was discovered ten minutes later in the grounds, digging a hole. The sergeant, who had long since despaired of finding the right scent, then announced that he would take the dog for one last frisk before retiring to the station. This was a good cue for making some tea; and, with Pluto contentedly munching an underdone sausage from the night-nurses' supper, a good time was had by all.

The Lancet, January 1955

* * * *

Our anaesthetist's small daughter ran impetuously down the garden path to fling herself into his waiting arms. She tripped over a stone and went tumbling to the ground.

'Daddy kiss it better,' she sobbed, and this simple remedy certainly worked wonders.

---

4. A simple faint.

'Did you make lots of people better today?' she asked, when the flow of tears had subsided. Not without modesty, he answered in the affirmative.

'And did you kiss them all?'

The Lancet, February 1955

* * * *

Hopes of a cure for arteriosclerosis have been revived by exciting news from China. Scientists have long been puzzled by the apparent immunity of the Chinese to arteriosclerosis. Therefore, the discovery of a new drug, prepared from the muck-weed *yen wu pong* and given the approved name of hydroxypropyl-*nor*-yen-wupongine, is not without interest.

The credit for the first thorough investigation must go to the workers at Barthomary's Hospital, where seven patients with thickening of the radial arteries were given HNYWP by continuous intragastric drip for 47 hours. Careful palpation of both radial arteries only three months later showed complete arrest of the disease process in no less than 71% of cases. One patient died of coincidental lymphosarcoma and one took his own discharge. In the light of these findings, further investigation was deemed reasonable.

A large-scale clinical trial was then instituted by the Arteriosclerosis Research Panel, urgently formed by fellows of the Royal Colleges with a personal interest in the problem. The panel was commendably cautious in its interpretation of the Barthomary series, since no controls were used, and wisely insisted that the trial should include at least 5,000 treated and untreated cases. Also, in view of the need for certain special clinical and pathological observations – e.g., pulse and sedimentation rate – supplies of HNYWP were restricted to the teaching hospitals. A shortage of clinical material proved an early obstacle and it was found necessary to appeal for suitable cases of essential hypertension, coronary sclerosis, cerebral thrombosis, gangrene, and senile dementia. It is only fitting to record the magnificent and magnanimous response by most non-teaching hospitals.

Some important facts were brought to light. For instance, it was conclusively established that where both cerebral hemispheres had softened as the result of haemorrhage, the lesion was irreversible and the administration of HNYWP could serve no useful purpose. No definite conclusions could be reached as to the earlier claims from China and Barthomary's, but it was recommended that provincial hospitals undertake further trials. The panel added the interesting observation that a statistically significant number of chronic bronchitics were afforded symptomatic relief during the trial.

The Lancet, April 1955

* * * *

In our little town, local pride boasts of three claims to fame – its salubrious salts, its generous accommodation for the mentally afflicted, and its Derby. Upon the downs, the hygroscopic chemicals in the soil give the turf an invigorating springiness which seems to communicate itself to the race-goers; and for those with time for reflection there is always the magnificent view of the pinnacles of the great mental institutions. There is a theory, popularly held after a trying outpatient session, about the indifferent mental health enjoyed by a singularly large section of the local population. This claims that many ex-patients settle here and raise families, for even they are aware of the unique attributes of the district.

On Derby Day one receives the distinct impression that all three major industries combine to ensure its success. Red-hot tips issue forth like sparks from a furnace and many a credulous victim has cause for regret after the race. The afternoon's work necessarily ceases, and those with outpatient appointments are seized with a sudden, though temporary, zest for fresh air. Among inpatients, no-one is too ill to take an interest in the commentary; and preparations usually begin in the morning with a popular clamour for the famous salts, whose pharmacological effect is ideally calculated to relieve all concerned from distracting thoughts at an exciting moment later in the day.

This year proved no exception in that losses were many and winnings were few. An inevitable gloom descended on the wards, impoverished tendon reflexes and sub-normal evening temperatures were common, and the prospect of a forthcoming election failed to lift the depression. The only optimism sprang from a few undesirable characters who presented themselves at the casualty door in the hope of a night's bath, board and lodging, and theirs was short-lived.

The Lancet, June 1955

* * * *

Billy was an inveterate burglar. Having had rheumatic fever at an age too innocent to be anything other than honest, the old heart valves were at last giving way under the constant strain of his nefarious activities. As a result, he was in and out of hospital almost as often as he was in and out of gaol. He would come in with legs like king-sized sausages, neck veins up to his ears and his liver saying how-d'ye-do to the umbilicus. Six months' hard labour (for us that is) and we would just about have him fit enough to go home. But there was the rub, for no sooner was he out of hospital when he would go burgling again, which inevitably put him back into cardiac failure. If climbing the rooftops did not bring it on, then evading the long arm of the law did, and, his exercise tolerance being what it was, there was a fifty-fifty chance of him coming into hospital or gaol. In the event of the latter and a remnant of cardiac reserve, he would be sent down for hard labour which invariably sent him into failure and the prison hospital.

Considering the life he led and the state of what he was pleased to call his 'ticker', he had done well to live to the ripe old age of 65, which in most professions is looked upon as a suitable age to retire from active duties. Exasperated by his multitudinous admissions to both hospital and gaol, we thought fit to tackle him on this score one day.

'Now, look here,' we pointed out, 'this is no way to go on for a man of your years. Surely, it's high time you retired. All these months in gaol are bound to number your days.'

'As a matter of fact, guv'ner, that's where you're wrong,' he replied. 'You'll be interested to know in there the food's better, the bed's better and, if you'll pardon me for saying so, the medical attention's better.'

The Lancet, August 1955

* * * *

The fame and tradition of our hospital is such that we are rarely without guests from foreign lands. Last week we entertained a party of distinguished American visitors, and showing them round proved a most agreeable task. Clinical demonstrations of rare and interesting conditions aroused their admiration, and in one corner alone no less than five examples of a new disease could be seen. And by television, intricate operations were relayed direct from the theatre with such startling perfection of technique that not a few physician-viewers came away with the impression that opening the chest was simpler than auscultating it.

The morning was given up to conducted tours of the hospital, and it was as well that administrative foresight had offered us the previous day a concentrated refresher course in the art of guidemanship. It would certainly never have occurred to me that 400 dustbins were in use at any one time, or that in the bowels of the basement a gigantic bin-washing apparatus daily rendered them as sterile as milk-churns. Nevertheless, it had to be conceded that, by and large, there was little Uncle Sam could not make bigger and better. And, sure enough, it soon transpired that their enuretic children were twice as big and twice as many as ours.

Highlights of the tour included curious items. Our scales, for instance, were in great demand. 'It sure is kind of swell getting weighed in genuine stones and ounces,' one of the visitors explained. But the morning did not pass without misunderstandings. It was difficult to explain the surgeons' neglect of the title 'Dr', and its indiscriminate use by those who are merely 'bachelors', a term which, in turn, applied equally well to married men or female graduates. Then we came upon a door marked ALMONER, whereupon the proverbial generosity of Americans sprang to light, for, like a conditioned reflex, there was an instant reaching for pocket-books, which was restrained only with difficulty. Our last (and, perhaps, most lasting) misunderstanding concerned that wholly British institution, the ward sister.

Some of our guests thought of her as a charitable body who devoutly spent her off-duty in a cloister; others thought that she was a young nurse who did not discourage expressions of familiarity. They were introduced to the real thing, after which no-one was left in doubt on the latter score.

The Lancet, August 1955

* * * *

The *bruit d'airain* of pneumothorax is still taught in all medical schools, although extensive research has recently cast discredit on its value as a physical sign. Commonly known as the 'bell' or 'coin' sound, it would seem that more is involved than the mere jangling of one coin on another.

The position of the coin in relation to the stethoscope is an important and much-neglected detail. Using a photo-electric thoracometer with a differential action potential of ten decibels, it was found that the sound waves in a fur-stripped cat were no less absent in pneumothorax than in a dead animal. Only by inflating both lungs with a mixture of oxygen and radioactive uranium was it possible to produce a low-pitched sonorous undertone, likened to the rumble of distant thunder.

Such factors as the rate, force, and frequency of percussion were also considered in great detail. A special electrically powered percussor was devised into which six patients could be strapped at one time. In this way it was hoped to eliminate individual idiosyncrasy, so common in an experiment of this kind. It was conclusively shown that, with a frequency of 100 strokes per second at a pressure of 300 lb per square inch, the true *bruit d'airain* was indistinguishable from sounds produced by borborygmi in the sigmoid colon, air-locks in the central heating, or the time signal on the radio.

Ambitious experiments were also conducted on the metallurgic properties of plessor and pleximeter. An interesting phenomenon occurred in many subjects when a 10-franc piece was struck with the Hungarian pengő. The result, paradoxically, could best be described by the sound made when the lid of a half-filled samovar is lightly tapped with the wooden handle of a twelve-gauge screwdriver. The investigators concluded that if this physical sign is to be elicited at all, the common penny must be discarded in favour of the Colombian peso. It would appear therefore that the test as ordinarily performed gives no reliable evidence of air in the chest.

The Lancet, August 1955

* * * *

The instinct whereby birds migrate across continents and eels swim thousands of miles to the Sargasso Sea, is rare in *Homo sapiens*. But somewhere in the heart of Surrey stands a small hospital which has that effect on whoever may once have dangled a stethoscope within its walls. By tradition, no member of the medical staff leaves without a farewell celebration to which residents and consultants, past and present, migrate mysteriously and with unerring instinct. And since tenures of office are continually drawing to a close, each new ceremony tends to become bigger and better than the last.

The way these gatherings come about is a matter for conjecture. Some say that it is the ceremonial hot punch

– the secret of which is handed down from generation to generation of resident anaesthetist – which calls the clan together. But then, this strange instinct has been felt beyond England's northern border, and it seems hardly credible that Sassenach smells can be detected in the homeland of whisky.

The fact remains that, several times a year, peripatetic inclinations are irresistibly drawn to the verdant beauty of Surrey. Before nightfall, I find myself passing through those well-beloved gates, where a familiar ditch traps the unwary and the porter is always asleep; past the flag-pole regularly adorned with some object carefully selected to arouse the secretary's spleen; up the central ramp which serves as the main corridor and can, in practice, accommodate a pre-war Austin 7; in the direction of distant gramophone music and the occasional strains of a badly played violin, to the medical officers' mess where a spirited party is already in full swing.

Seeing so many old friends in a familiar setting produces the strange feeling that nothing has changed and that time has stood still. But the illusion is always broken by someone who has a new job, car, or wife; or who proudly shows photographs of three offspring instead of two; or who has at last passed the Membership,[5] only to find himself deprived of his premier pastime for the past ten years.

The Lancet, September 1955

* * * *

In recent months, the attention of paediatricians has focused on a mysterious disease, hitherto unknown, the protean

---

5. Membership of the Royal College of Physicians, attainable by examination.

manifestations of which have been recognised as forming the Davy Crockett[6] syndrome. Pandemic in distribution, equally prevalent in both sexes, and with no respect for site or season, it has become increasingly clear that a new clinical entity has appeared. While the most florid examples of the condition are to be found in childhood, a not uncommon secondary form of the syndrome also occurs in adult life.

This fascinating disease may present in all manner of guises and almost all the special departments of a hospital may meet with one or other of the many clinical variants. In skin clinics, the characteristic coronal distribution of the lesions extending band-wise to the skin of the cervical and upper thoracic spine, should give rise to no difficulty. Outbreaks of spring catarrh and hay-fever, in the absence of both spring and hay, may perplex ophthalmologists and ENT surgeons, whilst allergists may be misled by extraordinary reactions to scratch-testing with the usual allergens. Gastro-intestinal disturbances are not infrequent and a Davy Crockett trichobezoar[7] is a recognised complication. Some of the features of the syndrome have been attributed to an increase in mouse-borne infections on the grounds that the heavy demand for feline fur has left an insufficient number of cats to keep the mouse population down to a sanitary

---

6.   In 1954, Walt Disney televised the adventures of Davy Crockett, a 19th-century American folk hero, frontiersman and soldier, in a five-part series. In the series, Crockett wore a quirky, raccoon-fur hat complete with bushy tail that dangled from the back. For four or five years, millions of children (and, as Dad recalls, some adults too) would not be seen dead without their prized coonskin hats on their heads. At the height of their popularity in the 1950s, children's coonskin caps sold at an average of five thousand per day and spawned some 100 million dollars' worth overall. Indeed, the fad for wearing a Davy Crockett hat might be seen as the forefather of today's media-driven pop fads, something which Dad abhorred and ridiculed in equal measure.

7.   A mass of undigested hair within the gut.

level. Several paediatricians have expressed the view that enuresis,[8] constipation, and acidosis are also part of the syndrome, but the evidence is not convincing. However, psychological disturbances are certainly encountered and usually take the form of outbursts of aggressive behaviour. It has been shown that, in most cases, such behaviour is due to the social inferiority consequent upon *not* possessing a Davy Crockett hat.

The Lancet, November 1955

* * * *

The somatic physician who goes digging in the psychiatrists' garden is in for a bewildering experience. It is like groping one's way in a darkroom with both feet off the floor; and as one's eyes become accommodated to delicate shades of grey, one surprise follows another.

Ward rounds are particularly strange. Instead of moving from bed to bed inquiring: 'How are you?' I now pass from chair to chair asking for the name of the Prime Minister. One patient gave me a cheery 'Good morning!', but when I told the psychiatrist, he said: 'I know, poor soul, she is very disturbed.' Several mornings are spent in the production of convulsions and coma, and I find it difficult to keep my thoughts from the many sleepless nights I had doing the opposite. Apparently the TV is the biggest boon to psychiatrists since electricity was invented; all programmes from the interludes to *Puzzle Corner* are followed with rapt attention. *Punch* is heavily subscribed to, and even in the doctors' mess a pile of copies holds pride of place next to *The Lancet*.

Relatives have to be interviewed the whole time, not

8.   Bed-wetting.

so much with the idea of imparting information as to ascertain the aberration in themselves which precipitated the patient's trouble. However, I had to sympathise with the husband who told me how it all began with his daughter's blinking eyes. The school nurse said it was a cold, the doctor conjunctivitis, and the optician short sight. They went to a specialist in Harley Street who said it was astigmatism and ordered reading glasses, but another specialist in Wimpole Street ordered distance glasses, while a third specialist at the hospital said that no glasses were needed at all. 'The wife has been confused ever since,' he explained.

The Lancet, January 1956

* * * *

Jimmy was seven years old and had leukaemia. Christmas was near when his mother and father learned the truth. The tragedy of medicine lay bare: neither compassion nor the faintest glimmer of a last hope could soften the cold truth. 'We can do nothing. A few weeks, perhaps; that's all; nothing more. Only a miracle could – '

With treatment, Jimmy gradually improved. On Christmas Day, he sat up in bed surrounded by toys and sweets, and his face shone with soap, joy, and cortisone. Soon his blood was normal and his marrow too; his spleen could no longer be felt, and his once-enlarged glands had vanished. And his appetite knew no limits. 'That's not the way to eat your dinner!' Sister was heard to cry. 'Haven't you got a knife and fork?' Chips, ice cream, strawberry jam, and Tizer were his favourites, and on this diet he rapidly made up the weight he had lost. The day came when he was ready to go home. His pyjamas and slippers were put in a small suitcase, and, with trousers, pullover, coat and school cap, he walked slowly through the hospital gates between his mother and father.

That was two years ago. Since then Jimmy has had another Christmas, and two birthdays, two Easters, and five school holidays. He was happy enough before his illness, but each month his parents tried to bring him even more happiness, knowing that it might be his last. Thrice more he walked out through the hospital gates. But the fourth time he was carried by his father, and last week he died.

Philosophers may argue that two years is a fleeting moment in the life of a little boy; that he might have found a greater peace in death two years ago than in two years hence; that a single sorrow borne once is lighter than many borne often. But the light in the eyes of Jimmy and his parents knew nothing of philosophy. We have no regrets.

The Lancet, January 1956

* * * *

Dear Hawke,[9]

Mrs Neal has just gone out again. This time she stayed in hospital for over two weeks, she had seven pints of blood, and her haemoglobin rose from 34% to 65%.

You may have good cause for satisfaction. When somebody has had forty-three pints of blood, the uneventful transfusion of a further seven is an achievement on which the pathologist can just look with pride. Thanks to you and your colleagues, a blood-transfusion is probably the simplest and safest life-saving operation in the whole of

---

9.   A fictional haematologist – my father's invention!

medicine. The meticulous care taken in the collecting, and in your grouping and matching, is almost enough to eliminate hazards at your end; when the occasional mishap does occur, we all know that we must first look for the cause ourselves. Even the blood of Mrs Neal, with its antibodies and its hyperglobulins, is a poor challenge to your resourcefulness. Your modest labels reading 'Compatible Washed Cells' do not deceive me as to the vast amount of work they conceal. Mrs Neal has had her sixteenth transfusion without batting an eyelid.

Yes, you may well be satisfied. But, as her physician, I am not. Seven pints is a lot of blood; but 65% is a long way from 100%, and two weeks is a long time.

I have worked out that, for her sixteen transfusions, Mrs Neal has spent a total of close on five months in hospital. Members of the committee might well throw up their hands in horror and weep over the £19-odd that it costs to maintain one bed in our hospital for one week; but far more important considerations are at stake. Often we have been very short of beds and have had to refuse admissions because Mrs Neal was taking up a bed. For a time, we tried taking her in when the blood was ready, but you never sent enough and she still had to wait another week for the second instalment. We tried giving her a few surreptitious bottles from our emergency stock, but you found out and made a fuss. We persuaded her relations to become donors, but it has made no difference.

Of course, Mrs Neal is no less anxious to get out of hospital than we are to expedite her return home. Last summer we tried to top her up for her summer holiday, but you could not spare the blood in time. We had to keep her in over Christmas for the same reason. Your explanation for the delay is always the same. Group-0 Rh-negative blood is precious and the demand is heavy. The need is more urgent elsewhere. Sometimes there is an exchange transfusion for rhesus incompatibility, and this must come first.

So you see, this problem goes deeper and deeper, until it reaches our fundamental medical and other principles. Is the life of this patient, whose aplastic marrow renders her dependent on the blood of others, any more or any less important than that of a jaundiced newborn babe? Are we to set ourselves up in judgement and say: 'This life is worth preserving but that one is not'?

Mrs Neal is a simple soul. She does not know what is wrong with her, and would not understand if we told her. She has no special gifts and her education leaves much to be desired. She has no hobbies and would be hard-pressed to say what she does with herself all day. At 60, she feels she has earned a rest and therefore lets the younger members of the family attend to the work. Not that she appreciates her family any more than she appreciates all the medical attention she is having. It would certainly never occur to her that fifty donors have given their blood freely to keep her alive for a year. Instead, she nurses a deep resentment against all of us because we cannot cure her at less inconvenience to herself. Her simple mind cannot understand why she has to have transfusions when her friends and neighbours are revived by a few iron or vitamin pills.

Many would say, here is a worthless life if ever. Society could suffer no loss by her untimely end. Her relations may well feel relieved of their burden. A hospital bed would be freed.

One can argue that when a man is struggling in the final stages of some fatal disease it is kindness to let him die peacefully. There comes a time when penicillin may thoughtlessly deprive some age-wracked body of its last friend. It is as well if the infant imbecile need never open its eyes upon a cruel world.

In all this I confess my guilt; but I cannot place Mrs Neal in the same category. Are you going to abandon someone who openly demands life as her birthright? Are you, who holds the elixir of life, prepared to accept this terrible responsibility?

There can be few of us who would not shrink from such a task. When Bernard Shaw wrote of *The Doctor's Dilemma* he could scarcely have guessed the reality of the plot. You will remember, the choice between the deserving colleague and the undeserving genius was not made lightly. Your choice, made from the meagre date on a slip of paper, is all the harder. I do not blame you for making a compromise. What can be simpler than to share the elixir?

For my part, I've always thought it my duty to put relief of suffering before everything else – even before the saving of life. It comforts me to know that, however incurable the disease, there is always something I can do. But for once I am powerless.

Anaemia is not usually a distressing complaint. Mrs Neal, however, is elderly and her arteries are hard and narrow. Her lungs are emphysematous, her heart is weak, her eyesight is poor. Her gastric mucous membrane is atrophic, and her digestion is not good. When her haemoglobin falls below 60% she begins to get angina, breathlessness, and cramp. She loses appetite and weight, and even medicine gives her indigestion. As her legs gradually swell, so her body slows and her mind becomes dull. Finally, her haemoglobin 35%, she is reduced to the picture of abject misery that I know so well. She comes to us for help. And what do we do? We transfuse her till her haemoglobin is 65%; and five days later the whole wretched story begins all over again. You have made your compromise.

I admit we are no nearer to a solution, although I hope I have convinced you that, of the possibilities, at least two are unacceptable. Surely there must be an answer to the problem that does not clash with one's ideals? I should willingly do anything in my power to help you find it.

Forgive me for taking you from your microscope.

Yours ever,

Herbert

The Lancet, March 1956

* * * *

The time has come when physicians should band together and defy the serious menace to their art which noisily fills our skies. It is virtually impossible now to use the stethoscope without the disturbing buzz of aircraft overhead. As one strains ecstatically for the rarest râle[10] or the most musical of murmurs, one's senses are instantly shattered by the irreverent coughing and spluttering of these infernal engines. And the poignancy of the moment is the greater when one has just taken infinite pains and achieved infinite unpopularity in commandeering silence from the ceaseless chattering and sluice-clatter that pervade all hospital wards.

The solution clearly does not lie with peaceful approaches. I have waited impatiently for a lull before running from patient to patient with chest-piece poised aloft. I have closed windows, I have bought thick rubber tubing, I have wound cotton-wool round my ear-pieces and I have shaken my fist in the air – all to no avail. No sooner do I reach for my stethoscope when a distinct drone revives my frustration. And as I stand by helpless while opening

---

10. An abnormal rattling sound heard in the lungs.

snaps and bronchial breathing go undetected, the drone becomes a crescendo of deafening vibrations, enough to discomfort Laennec[11] in his place of rest.

The problem is urgent, for if a solution is not found soon, we shall have to throw away our stethoscopes and carry mechanical phonograms instead. Even so, we shall have to learn how to decipher the graphic squiggles of aeroplanes from those produced within our patients' chests.

The Lancet, April 1956

* * * *

The paraplegic in our ward needed a new self-propelling chair and, to set the wheels in motion, the official request form was properly signed, countersigned, sealed, and sent off with the blessings of even the hospital secretary. In the good old days, when a spade was a spade, a chair was also a chair, but such simple considerations are no longer what they were. We now have big chairs and little chairs; we have chairs with larger wheels in front and those with smaller wheels behind; some are made of wicker, some of wood, and some of iron; some take up more room than a bedstead, while others can be folded up and carried about. There are a hundred-and-one other refinements – straight backs with round seats, round backs with square seats, and square seats with round holes. The matter is clearly one for a specialist, and in due course we had word that the Ministry's Senior Wheelchair Consultant was on his way.

Hasty arrangements were made so that everything would be ready on his arrival. The patient's bi-weekly bath was antedated, fresh flowers appeared on the bedside

---

11. Inventor of the stethoscope.

locker, and the house-physician brought the notes up to date. At last he arrived, armed to the teeth with official-looking documents. Irrelevant items, such as obstetric history and the width of the neighbours' front garden gate, were painstakingly recorded, and then he asked to see the patient. To our amazement, he confined himself to a detailed dental examination and, carefully noting that 70% of the upper and 100% of the lower teeth were false, he packed his instruments and left.

Not only are we sorely perplexed – we are exceedingly worried. All this happened six months ago and the patient has since had the left upper canine extracted. Will the wheelchair, when it comes, still fit?

The Lancet, April 1956

* * * *

A year ago the first report of HNYWP (hydroxypropyl-*nor*-yen-wupongine), the citronella-soluble extract of the Chinese muck-weed *yen wu pong*, appeared in these columns. Since then, research centres have sprung up all over the world, lecture tours have been given in four continents, and in Cameria the first university chair of yenwupongology has been established. A world YWP congress is to take place in the Canary Isles this summer and the *Quarterly Journal of Yenwupongology* is in its third quarter. A new qualification, for which several enterprising institutions conduct postgraduate courses, has already been set up and the MRCP(Y) is expected to become an essential pre-requisite in future consultant appointments. The impact of the discovery has not been without political repercussions. Talks at the highest level have reaffirmed multinational faith in peaceful co-existence, export restrictions of muck-weed have been lifted, and an expedition of botanists has gone to China to study oriental fertilisers.

In England, the newly appointed yenwupongine travelling research fellow has drawn attention to the dearth of scientific baseline data. His first task has been to launch a survey into the natural history of arteriosclerosis, and questionnaires have been circulated to all general practitioners. Unfortunately, many were invalidated by improper replies, although each form was accompanied by a 120-page explanatory booklet. However, past impressions that arteriosclerosis is not incompatible with longevity would appear to be substantiated and credit must go to the fellows of the two influential London clubs who have temporarily buried the gold-headed hatchet and jointly sponsored this investigation.

A new line of research is already bearing fruit at the Guysex Free Hospital where intensive work is being done on the arterial disease of the crocodile. Since the ophthalmoscopic findings of exudates, haemorrhages and a-v nipping are similar to those found in man, the crocodile would appear to be an optimal experimental model if certain technical difficulties can be overcome.

Meanwhile, at St Barthomary's Hospital, clinical studies continue. Two active principles have been isolated – yenwupongine and yenwupongeine. Both, when suspended in vitriol and administered by surreptitious injection, produce infiltration, perivascular necrosis and refusal to submit to further treatment. This phenomenon, known as Ducane's triple response, is thought to arise at some point in the cranio-tarsal axis. Other toxic side effects include leucocytosis, leucopenia, frequency, oliguria, euphoria, depression, obesity, weight loss, diarrhoea and constipation.

Clearly, the theoretical justification for yenwupongine has not been fully realised and it is not free from hazard. But the physician has found an unusual new chemical tool which may yet lead to a better understanding of a common disease of today.

The Lancet, May 1956

* * * *

Miss Jenkins's greatest mistake, I suppose, was to take her baby to the hospital. I could easily have dealt with the situation – that irritating triviality of an infant's nether region for which paediatricians seem unable to find a scientific name. But this time it had to be the hospital.

The earnest young doctor at the hospital carefully avoided the morals of the case, but, finding that the baby had a small head and a systolic murmur, immediately accused Maisie of having had German measles six months previously, which she stoutly denied. A conference with the registrar, assistant, and chief followed, and one by one they all had a go, but she remained adamant. The almoner was summoned to tempt her with home-helps, meals-on-wheels, and all the panacea of the welfare State, if only she would change her mind. When the gentle methods of the almoner had failed, sterner measures were applied. Maisie was kept waiting about in the outpatient department, which was not very difficult to arrange, and was interrogated by a different doctor each time, which was even less difficult. Sometimes a succession of students was sent to torment her, all with the same question. She was assigned to one of the ward-sisters, who had a well-earned reputation for the difficult case, but still her story remained unshaken.

A series of clinical conferences was given in her presence when the chief made a great point of demonstrating the baby as an example of the rubella syndrome. Everybody referred to the baby knowledgeably as 'that RS' and the registrar wrote in his summary '...undoubtedly a classical case, although the mother has not admitted it yet.' Maisie was weakening physically but stuck to her guns, and her resistance became acutely embarrassing to the hospital authorities. Every now and then a tactless student would ask why she had not had rubella; her notes could not be accurately coded and were always getting lost; no treatment could be started until the other business had been cleared up. It grew out of all proportion and became one of the most pressing research projects. A succession of young doctors tried their hand, but matters came to a head when one of them decided to write an article. A confession, a written one at that, was now imperative. No-one will ever know how he managed it. But after nearly two hours, he emerged from behind closed doors, clutching a piece of paper which bore the cryptic message:

'I now admit I had German measles while I was carrying,
Signed MAISIE JENKINS.'

The other day I came across an article describing some allegedly rare combination of troubles after maternal rubella. It's a pity he went to all that trouble, because I could have told him that Maisie had had two others just like it. I could have told him about the village odd-job man – he's got a small head too. But then, I wasn't asked.

The Lancet, September 1956

* * * *

His father died the day before his 100th birthday and his grandfather lived to 103. Is it any wonder that old Bingle, at 94, considered himself a mere chicken? After his bout of pneumonia we sent him to *Blackstones* – a large tumbledown house miles from nowhere, where sixty-year-old men eke out their remaining span.

Old people need a corner of their own, and Bingle found his corner quickly. 'I'm not stoppin' here unless I can work,' he declared. Matron understood – besides, she was short of staff. A remarkable worker he turned out to be. He made his bed, he swept the floors, he cleaned the cutlery ('the silver', he called it), and tended his little patch in the garden. Then, at the end of the day's work, came his special privilege and his alone. With rolled-up sleeves and apron, he would sit in the kitchen with Cook, a glass of beer at his elbow and a smouldering pipe in his mouth. He never said anything but just sat, impassive, like any honest labourer at home when day is done.

One morning he awoke with a streaming cold. Amid noisy bouts of coughing and sneezing, he prepared to follow his normal routine. He was donning his apron when Matron saw him. Pleading, argument, and persuasion all fell on deaf ears. All his life he had never stopped work for a common cold and he saw no reason to change his ways. Their voices rose, words became harsh. 'But you are old!' cried Matron, like the young man in *Alice*, and snatched the apron, which he was clutching desperately, from his grasp. With a terrible rending sound, one half of it came away in her hands. At this Bingle grew quiet and allowed himself to be hustled back to bed.

When dinner was served, he was missing. A search of the house and grounds was begun at once but it was futile, for his bed was tidy and his locker bare. There was no help for it but to inform the police, and search parties were soon under way. He was found the same afternoon, stick in one hand and his few belongings in the other, having covered nearly ten of the thirty miles to his daughter's cottage. They brought him back unrepentant and defiant.

I was glad he got no further. Now he need never know his daughter has been gone these six months – she was over seventy when she died. He need never know his loneliness.

The Lancet, October 1956

* * * *

Last Sunday, soon after the night nurses came on duty, the patient at the far end of the ward developed more pain and the house-physician was summoned. Five minutes later, nineteen pairs of eyes watched curiously as he made his way down the length of the ward and back. He thought the patient too ill to have an operation and he telephoned his chief. Twenty minutes later, all eyes turned as the physician, accompanied by his house-physician and the nurse, marched briskly to the far end of the ward. He thought that an operation, although indicated, carried considerable risk and called in the surgeon. To the inhabitants of a medical ward, the appearance of a surgeon is always regarded with grave misgivings, and all eyes were agog when the procession of four set out on the journey to the end of the ward some twenty minutes later. In the opinion of the surgeon, the operative risk was negligible compared to the risk of the anaesthetic, and the anaesthetist was invited to express an opinion. Soon after, a wakeful ward watched a quintet of specialists and auxiliaries on their pilgrimage to the last bed.

Now anaesthetists, like spectators at a football match, are often inspired to a plan of action not readily apparent to the principal combatants. Thus the anaesthetist opined that the risk of the operation depended on the result of a blood test, and the pathologist was summoned. Twenty minutes later, he too ran the gauntlet of curious gazes as he negotiated the length of the ward. Few pathologists, called in to help with a difficult case, can resist suggesting a further investigation. The first blood test was normal, but the result of the second made an immediate X-ray examination imperative.

By this time, the area before the hospital main entrance was enough to set every National Health Service heart beating with pride. In an imposing row stood the parked cars of as many members of the staff as could be seen on any weekday. The physician's old Ford rubbed noses with the pathologist's A70, while the anaesthetist's Velox stood alone some distance away, because it was brand new. And when the brilliant headlights of the radiologist's Jaguar swept through the drive, hospital history was made.

The procession that entered the ward on its final journey brought a gasp of admiration from the two rows of figures sitting bolt upright in their beds. With bulging eyes, the nineteen heads swivelled slowly through a full semicircle. Gloriously, majestically, past went the consultants and specialists, the residents and nurses, and bringing up a triumphant rear, the crane-like apparatus of the portable X-ray, propelled by two porters.

It took all of us exactly four-and-a-quarters hour to decide to do nothing that night.

The Lancet, February 1957

* * * *

Among the blights of a casualty officer's life, the common tramp looms large. Joshua Smallpiece was the exception to prove the rule.

He looked about 80, but he might have been 100 for all we knew. He had a grey, verminous beard which reached down to the waist and he wore dirty old rags for clothing. After his first admission, these were hastily burnt and he complained bitterly about this affront. Neither boots nor socks, he claimed, had left his feet for two-and-a-half years, and the students who had assisted in their removal saw no reason to doubt his word.

In his way, he was a great naturalist. His favourite resting-place lay under the bridge by the river, and in time even the records department came to recognise this as his official residence. He lived with the birds and the trees and suffered with the elements. In the summer he had sunstroke, in the winter frostbite; the spring showers brought crippling arthritis, while November would bring him cyanosed and gasping feebly, as the fog seeped through his lungs. One icy Christmas Day, he slipped and broke his wrist. The nurses did a wonderful job disinfesting his beard, and he was the best Father Christmas the hospital has ever known.

Joshua never outstayed his welcome. The first sign of recovery would find him sitting in the grounds on the old wooden bench, throwing crumbs to the pigeons. We sometimes thought they knew him, for there were always more of them when he was about. But as soon as the strength came back to his legs, nothing would hold him; with his stick and his bundle, he was off on the road, and the long shaggy beard would once again become a familiar sight by the river's edge. He had a strange superstition concerning his beard, for he would never allow a single hair to be cut. 'The day you take my beard off, I die,' he said. He looked as if he meant it and his wishes were respected.

One thundery autumn day, he was brought in unconscious, the victim of a stroke. For two days he lay in coma, the long grey beard trailing over his paralysed body like a bale of tow. The ward was busy and staff was short. 'Shave the old man in the corner,' called the nurse in charge. But the ward had four corners, an old man in each. It was too late. Joshua's features, seen by us for the first time, showed a ghostly pallor, his expression one of terrible reproach. That evening he wept like a child, and by midnight he was dead.

The Lancet, March 1957

* * * *

Contrary to prevailing beliefs, most of the great advances in medicine are born in humble places. History recently repeated itself when a quiet country town in a little-known corner of the West Country gently turned a new page in the annals of social medicine.

The ever-dwindling demand for Infant Welfare Centres has been the subject of many important discussions, but at last one Medical Officer of Health has acted upon the courage of his convictions by closing his down completely and inaugurating in its place a new 'Welfare Clinic for Old People'. Housed in the same building and staffed by the same doctors, nurses and helpers, this marks a brave beginning to face the reality of a changed social scene.

The simple opening ceremony brought feelings of sadness and regret, and a few onlookers wept silently. A sturdy apple-cheeked toddler skipped on and off the scales to symbolise the end of the children's clinic. His great-grandmother, at ninety-three the town's oldest inhabitant, was then lifted onto the same scales. And as she was helped down, frail, wrinkled and trembling, her grand-daughter stepped forward to receive two specially inscribed spoons to commemorate the occasion. Thus a span of four generations saw the passing of the new for the old.

Those familiar with the past were able to detect a few subtle alterations. The tiny stools had been cleverly turned into footrests and were ranged before a row of straight-backed Windsor chairs. Where once a pile of toy bricks had been, now lay a box of dominoes. The old rocking horse, battered by the play of countless children, was no more; a fine new rocking chair stood in its place. And yet, much remained unchanged. The big white cupboard door still creaked to and fro on its hinges to reveal a generous stock of rubber sheets and cellulose napkins. There were packets of groats and bottles of orange juice on the table. The old pram shelter was crowded with invalid wheelchairs.

Outwardly the work of the clinic seems unchanged. Old people come along for regular checks on their general health, sight, hearing and dentures. But, most important of all, their daughters and daughters-in-law can find help, guidance and encouragement in the care of their elderly charges. They meet each other and compare notes, just as many of them used to do as young mothers, and they learn to take pride in what they do. They learn that gentleness and love mean even more to the very old than to the very young – that with all the well-meaning geriatrics in the world there's no place like home. Special son-and-daughter craft classes were arranged for the evenings after the old folks' bedtime to spread this renewed sense of responsibility.

Thoughtful onlookers at the inaugural ceremony will

remember particularly the closing words of the mayor's speech.

'Times do not change,' he said, 'it is people who change.'

The Lancet, April 1957

* * * *

Overheard in the Surgery. – 'Now never you mind about me, Sir, I'm all right. It's you we should be worried about. Why, just look at you. Your hands are all of a tremble and your legs are scarcely able to support you. You are an awful colour, and even your hair has turned a dirty grey. You must have lost pounds and pounds in weight because those clothes would look better on a broomstick. And as for those rings under your eyes – they're terrible! You know, you don't look a bit well. In fact, going downhill fast, that's what I should say you're doing. It's disgraceful that you should have to work in your condition. After all, your first duty to us patients is to look after yourself properly. I mean, what is to become of us patients if... I mean, we should never be the same without you if... well, you know what I mean. Now mind, you take care of yourself, and I had better come and see you again in two weeks' time, just to see how you are getting on.'

Follow-up?

The Lancet, June 1957

* * * *

I had some difficulty in making my American friend understand how to get to his destination.

'You take the left fork at the doss-house,' I explained.

'What's a doss-house?'

'A doss-house is a place where tramps put up for a night.'

'What's a tramp?'

'A vagrant, a vagabond, wayfarer, loafer...'

He looked at me blankly.

'A hoofer, a hobo, someone dressed in old clothes with a straggly beard who lives on the road,' I continued desperately.

'Now I get you,' he exclaimed at last. 'You mean a bum.'

The Lancet, June 1957

This and the four pieces that follow were written whilst my father was in Boston, Massachusetts.

* * * *

'Just another pneumonia, Sir.' Such was my introduction to William, a burly, self-conscious lad of twelve, lying rather awkwardly in bed, for he had reached an age when rapidly growing limbs seem at strange variance with a mind still that of a child. But why should a strapping lad have pneumonia at the height of summer? No-one could tell me, but something about his face made me pause and it was an unfilled line on his temperature chart which led us to his story.

He was seven years old when his mother died. For the next five years he was buffeted from relative to relative and house to house, some good, some bad, some kind, some harsh. Each move, bringing fresh problems, left its mark; but he learnt to imprison his unhappiness, and herein lay the root of the gradual atony which paralysed his colon, causing it to spill its contents like a brim-filled bowl.

After five years an indifferent succession of house-keepers came to an end. At last William came home – to a new home and to a new mother. When she welcomed him she did so wishing to love him as her own son. But on finding his soiled clothes in her laundry bag for the first time, she promptly remonstrated with her husband: 'Look what *your* son has given me to wash!' 'We'll soon see about that,' he said, and a few seconds later the hoarse cries of a broken-voiced adolescent tore through the house.

Uneasy peace reigned after this episode – uneasy because William sought to conceal his physical weakness by all possible means, for he alone knew that it lay beyond his control. He accumulated vast hoards of old rags and newspaper to insinuate between his clothes and skin. One night, after he had gone to bed, his father demanded the previous day's paper, and in a search from room to room they chanced upon his hoard – some used, waiting to be destroyed. 'There's only one way to cure him of this for once and for all,' said his father, making for the stairs. The bruises on his face, which had first arrested my attention, covered his body.

Doctors often scoff at the notion that pneumonia springs from cold and damp. The fact remains that this boy, forced to abandon his first defence, for five days washed his clothes in the river on his way home from school, donning the sogging garments each day before returning home. On the sixth day his breathing came in short, sharp gasps and he spat rusty sputum into his handkerchief. A doctor was summoned.

The Lancet, August 1957

* * * *

In this American town the ambulance with the most urgent note to its siren bears the inscription 'Dog Ambulance', and it can often be seen making, at breakneck speed, for the imposing 'City Hospital for Sick Animals (Inc.)'. According to our professor, whose dog once had its ears syringed there, the administrative efficiency of this institution might well be the envy of all the human hospitals. There is a comprehensive appointment system for all but acute emergencies, and patients are not kept hanging about in the waiting-hall. The house-officers wear name badges to facilitate rapport and lose no time in assigning Pluto to a ward – e.g., MDS, meaning male dog surgical – which is light and airy and has ample space between baskets. Special investigations, including blood chemistry and electrocardiography, are done by laboratories with a 24-hour service. Thus a cat in FCM began a diet of milk and fish on the day that a barium meal showed a duodenal ulcer.

There are three full-time psychiatrists on the staff, one with special training in psychoanalytic methods, while another had made a special study of the problems encountered in little dogs. Visiting hours are generous but nevertheless many patients require sedation. An attempt to avoid hospitalisation is reflected in the new outpatient department which is open day and night for emergencies, and accommodates many special clinics, as well as those for routine diagnosis and treatment. The allergy clinic is one of the most interesting, long courses of desensitising injections being given for various offending allergens, including human hair. A notable feature of the new building is the width of its entrance, because, it is rumoured, some years ago a circus elephant was rushed in with a suspected intussusception. Although so rare an exigency is unlikely to recur, a wide front door has proved its worth for the occasional cow admitted for her confinement.

The Lancet, March 1958

* * * *

Buying gas is one of the joys of American motoring. There is an indefinable thrill about pulling in at the gas station and giving the peremptory 'Fillerrup!' (preferably spoken out of the corner of the mouth). The novice need not be disconcerted if the attendant leaves the pump to churn by itself for a full five minutes while he busies himself with tyre pressures, battery, radiator water, and windshield. Some of those acromegalic saloons hold over twenty gallons, which, even so, will only come to six bucks (about forty shillings sterling). As a matter of fact, by going a little out of one's way, one can often save a few shillings, thanks to the gas wars. These arise because rival companies get it into their heads from time to time to see which can sell the cheapest petrol, which then gets cheaper and cheaper down the line until someone is actually selling the stuff at a loss. Of course nobody is prepared to keep this up for long, and a truce is usually called at this juncture. Meanwhile, delighted motorists rush back and forth, filling up anything they can lay their hands on. The arrangement is admirable for everyone, with the possible exception of the proprietor of the garage with the king-size discount. New Englanders, proud of their Scots blood, enter into the spirit of the gas wars with exceptional enthusiasm and will often go fifty miles out of their way to find the cheapest gas around town. Competition amongst garages is so keen that all kinds of inducements have to be thought up by imaginative proprietors. Some offer a 30-second-car-wash or a free change of muffler – i.e., a new silencer (you pay double for the silencer, but the screwing on and off is free). Slot-machines are popular bait, and most self-respecting garages have a drive-in Coca-Cola automat from which you can get your iced Coke without having to get out of the car. For some extraordinary reason, slot-machines for nail-clippers are also great favourites. An ingenious gimmick of one garage is to give away toll tickets for the bridge five miles up the highway, saving the casual motorist 25 cents, though the owner, who bought them by the month, paid only a fraction of this.

All this contrasts to the ill-treatment heaped on a submissive public by the British garage. It takes courage to ask to have one's windows wiped, and you have to be a long-standing customer of special merit before you are let in on the secret that the air-pressure gauge is not, and never has been, out of order. Particularly despicable is the cunning psychology behind the arrangement of the pumps, so that Super-Extra-Zing-Plus-Go is served by several pumps while the ordinary common-or-garden petrol (on which, as it happens, my car exceeds all expectations) has only one pump. Even if one has the will-power to face the long wait caused by this arrangement, one's temerity is likely to succumb to the second crafty ruse, whereby the one and only pump for ordinary petrol is placed at the approach of a narrow entrance so that a formidable traffic jam is apt to arise with startling and embarrassing rapidity. Then, over a cacophony of hooting, the pump attendant, with an expressive gesture of the thumb and in a voice tinged with the exactly right overtones of resignation, deprecation, and scorn, announces for all to hear: 'Yer can't move till 'e's 'ad 'is *cheap!*'

The Lancet, April 1958

* * * *

The world is full of those who decry everything that is English. Our weather is too cold, our climate too damp, our taxes too high and our buildings not high enough. Our buses are too full, our lives too empty, our shops too dull, our pageantry too showy, our clothes too woolly and our mutton too tough. Our sportsmen never win and our workers don't work. Our eggs are too cold, our music too modern, our politicians too many and our children too few. Yet despite my life-long familiarity with these national discrepancies, I must confess my first impression of the United States was of sheer topsy-turvy lopsidedness. Everything seems over the top – the buildings, the cars, the language, the dollar. My New York hotel was like a city itself with 24 floors, 2,000 rooms and its own shops and cinema, and a foyer the size of Waterloo Station. My bill for the night came to 12 dollars but the dollar is crazy – you get three for £1 and spend them like half-crowns.

The language takes some getting used to. Not only is it often incomprehensible but our coveted Queen's English is equally incomprehensible to the inhabitants. Fortunately this is not a bar to the rapid establishment of familiarity. The professor is Sam, my chief Joe, the intern Bob (pronounced Bub) and I am Herb. After all, we have known each other all of one hour.

On my second day Joe insisted I had dinner at his house. We started out from the hospital car park. Joe had some hard things to say about its inadequacy. If we had half a dozen car parks of similar size in Central London, parking would cease to be a problem. I asked him tentatively whether some of the difficulty might be due to the size of his and all the other cars. With massive bumpers, an elongated bonnet, three rows of seats, each wide enough for four adults to sit in comfort, and an enormous boot (trunk), it looked more at home at a bus stop than in a hospital car park. His reason for running this outsize vehicle was illuminating, since on an average outing with his three children, three dogs and friends of both children and dogs, he is if anything short of room. In fact, since a peaceful journey depends on sufficient distance between any two children and dogs, he often takes half the family in one car and his wife the other half in hers.

My encounter with the American medical student would fill more than a page and for the present I must end on the principal topic of the moment. It is on the radio, on the television and nobody appears to think of anything else. 'What exactly is the World Series?' I asked an appalled student. 'All the best baseball teams in the USA play each other until one of them wins four matches,' he explained slowly and patiently, as if to an idiot. 'What then?' I pressed him further. 'Why, they are the World Champions of course.'

The Lancet, May 1958

* * * *

It is an unhappy Christmas Day tradition in most hospitals for the senior surgeon to carve the ward turkey, usually with a display of ill-concealed inaptitude both anorexigenic and alarming to any patient about to undergo surgery. It is also customary to cast the paediatrician in the role of Father Christmas at the children's party and this, too, is an unsatisfactory arrangement.

To begin with, the disguise is hot and uncomfortable. One frequently trips over bits of trailing robe, and wisps of cotton wool have a propensity for invading oto-oro-rhinological orifices with irritating consequences which may render inadequate control over blasphemous interjection. For a few children the appearance of Father Christmas is the signal for a prolonged and piercing howl, unappeased by a chorus of a dozen shameless brats to the effect that 'He's not Father Christmas at all, but that nasty doctor who gave us the needle the other day!'

Having restored some semblance of order (a semblance being all that is ever feasible on these occasions), one must then begin the dangerous business of distributing the presents. The opening of the first parcel is the cue for a mad onrush of hordes of small children and, notwithstanding a bodyguard of stalwart nurses, the little horrors are liable to swamp trees, parcels, presents, Father Christmas, and everything. It is an unfortunate trend of our times to provide children with all manner of warring implements, and Father Christmas at once becomes the ready target for a variety of missiles ejected from crossbows, pop-guns, catapults, water pistols, and so on. Some of the little devils are so preoccupied with fighting that they fail to answer when their names are called. Then, every now and again, some juvenile impostor will claim a parcel destined for someone else, who soon raises a vociferous condemnation of this outrage. To mete out justice under these circumstances merely serves to transfer noise from one source to another. A final difficulty, for which there is no remedy, is that some child has to have his present last of all. A prolonged wait does nothing to enhance appreciation. Either he has one like it already only better, or it is the wrong colour, shape, or size, or perhaps neighbouring destructive influences are brought to bear at an early stage.

Thank heaven I have seen the last of Christmas for the next twelve months.

The Lancet, January 1960

* * * *

The other day I took my fountain pen to hospital. I hadn't an appointment, but the receptionist was sympathetic and said I could wait. I took a seat on a bench in the waiting-room alongside several other casualties. At the far end of the room, behind a long desk, uniformed clerks recorded pen-owners' complaints and undertook diagnostic examinations. Pens in need of specialised attention were whisked out of sight to an upstairs laboratory by vacuum cassettes. After a period of careful observation, I decided that outpatient therapy was not greatly favoured and that most pens were recommended admission for periods of up to a week. An ill-concealed despondency in prognosis was exemplified by a brisk trade at the new pens' counter.

When my turn came, I was agreeably surprised by the hygienic condition of the top of the desk considering the nature of most of the complaints, achieved no doubt by virtue of an unstinted stack of blotting-paper. (Paediatricians take note.) My clerk, an attractive girl in her early twenties, reminded me of a certain medical school, for her pen-side manner was coldly efficient and strictly impersonal. A few pointed, leading questions rapidly brought my rambling history to a close. The rest of the consultation was equally disconcerting. Wilful neglect on my part over the course of the years was the chief cause of my pen's breakdown, and the young lady did not mince her words.

'You've dropped it,' she accused me, having examined the nib at length with a magnifying glass. I protested my innocence but she obviously thought I was lying. 'How do you account for the fractured cover?' she demanded. 'You need a new barrel.' In the interests of economy I resisted. 'It affects your ink flow,' she warned, but I maintained the obstinate asininity of the layman, though luckily she did not make me sign a refusal-of-treatment form.

Next she squeezed all the ink out onto some blotting paper and examined it like a specimen of urine. 'Do you make a habit of mixing your inks?' she asked scathingly. 'No wonder your bladder is clogged.' (How is one to explain that sometimes and in all walks of life one may have to avail oneself of whatever facilities are conveniently at hand – e.g., dipping a gold nib into a National Health Service ink-pot?) 'It must go upstairs for a new bladder,' she prescribed finally. 'Will you leave it or wait?'

Obviously I waited, or I should not have been able to write this down.

The Lancet, July 1960

* * * *

In an old Chinese torture, water drips slowly onto the victim's head, the relentless, repetitive stimuli goading a frenzied nervous system to breaking point. Such was the state in which I found a colleague on Christmas Day.

It all began on Nov. 5 when he rashly promised his four-year-old-son a scooter for Christmas, provided his conduct in the interim was sufficiently exemplary to justify so lavish a gift. Thereafter, daily inquiries as to the advent of Christmas made increasing demands on my friend's self-control, culminating on Nov. 22 in a protracted, and at times falsetto, lecture to the effect that Christmas Day was synonymous with Dec. 25, which implied 33 days and 33 nights, 66 teeth-brushings, or the days needed to acquire 1s 4½d at the current rate of pocket money, and that further perseveration on the subject would invite stern counter-measures.

Left: Herbert
(left) with his
brother, Julian.
Berlin 1932.

Below:
Emil Bihari with sons,
Julian and Herbert
(far right).

Sitting on a log. Ida with sons, Julian and Herbert (*far right*).
Berlin, early 1930s.

Emil, Ida, Julian and Herbert *(second from left)* by the well outside Ida's parents' house in Czernica in Poland (now Ukraine) 1935.

Wynash Gardens in Carshalton, the Bihari's first home in England. The flats were built round a courtyard which contained a tennis court. This began for Herbert a lifelong passion for tennis. The area has since been grassed over.

Herbert and his mother in October 1940 – taken in Weston-super-Mare.

An early selfie? Writing for *The Lancet*. America, 1957.

Above: Spoof photos taken by Herbert using a timer were probably sent to his mother to show that he was able to look after himself. America, 1957.

Herbert supervising a child having her pulmonary function measured by a Collins water-seal spirometer.

Herbert and Dinah – circa 1964.

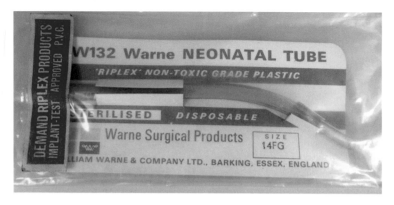

Early neonatal endotracheal tubes were made of rubber, but these caused irritation to babies' airways. Herbert switched to plastic - his 'St Thomas's tube' design became the forerunner of today's neonatal airways.

With thanks to Ballarat Base Hospital Trained Nurses League.

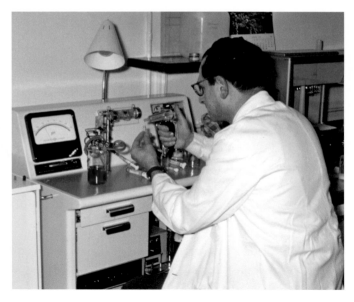

Herbert Barrie determining the arterial pH and base excess using the Astrup method.

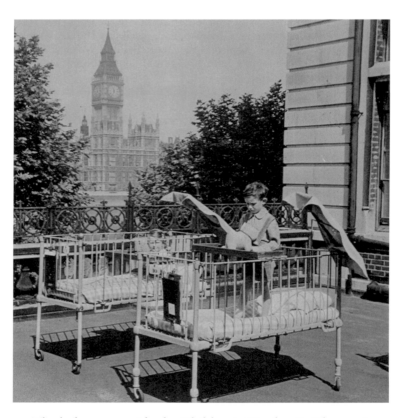

The balcony outside the Children's Ward at St Thomas's Hospital. Herbert's time at St Thomas's was probably the happiest of his professional life.

For the next thirteen days, this approach showed every sign of a well-earned success. Then, at the unfortunate time of 3.20am, a small voice was heard to say: 'Daddy, is it Christmas yet?' The resulting upheaval, awakening neighbours in four directions and causing many raised eyebrows on the train and curious glances in the launderette later that morning, can only be described as appropriate to minimising further miscalculations by a child reputed to be able to count to 100.

An uneasy peace reigned until Dec. 12, when, choosing the top of a crowded bus where chastisement could confidently be expected to arouse public hostility, the child observed half rhetorically 'Christmas is a long way off, isn't it?' which, under the circumstances, evoked nothing more than a monosyllabic assent and a somewhat excessive display of teeth. Fresh violence did not break out until the morning of Dec. 18 when, for an unaccountable reason, the wretched juvenile suddenly leapt out of bed and ran excitedly round the house yelling, 'Yippee, it's Christmas!' This provoked a course of action at once salutary and inhibitory to all further interest in the festive season.

As the appointed day approached, this conditioned apathy gave rise to concern and, inevitably, a remorseful parent sought to make amends by getting the finest scooter to be had. This was produced in all its glory on Christmas Day. The only comment its recipient made was: 'I don't think I want a scooter anymore, Daddy. Can I have a tricycle for next Christmas?'

The Lancet, January 1961

* * * *

A special congress of the Camerian Research Federation to commemorate the fourth anniversary of the discovery of yenwupongine,[12][13] was held on board the SS *Aurora* and in Honolulu last month.

Among the many important papers read out loud was an outstanding contribution by Abe Quabe,[14] Sam Finkelhoofer IV,[15] and Hyram D. Smith Jr,[16] describing their new bio-assay of HNYWP in the lacrimal fluid. Secretion, stimulated by a variety of ingenious techniques, was quantitated in a metrically calibrated transoptic circumferential container. Fractionated aliquots of the fluid, purified by papyraceous tissue filtration, were then eluted with unconjugated hydro-sulfated pseudo-chondroitin SO_4-B at pH 4.17, and the final solution injected into 8-week turkey embryos. Interference with a number of metabolic pathways resulted in a variety of developmental aberrations, including gonadal dysgenesis, as shown by abnormal comb growth in cocks and egg production in hens. The concentration of HNYWP in the lacrimal fluid could then conveniently be calculated from the formula:

$$C = 9.74 + P \times 4(N+\acute{K}) - 3\Delta\Sigma(HYWP) \div \sqrt{} \text{ eggs/week}$$

In the ensuing discussion, Dr Elmer Knut congratulated the authors on a swell piece of work. Dr Irving Katz expressed his delight that we were beginning to talk turkey

---

12. *The Lancet,* 1955, i, 917.

13. *Ibid,* 1956, i, 747.

14. Associate Professor of Clinical Yenwupongology, Department of Medicine, Yenwupongine Station and Research Laboratories, The Hiawatha Clinic and Hospital, Hiawatha Medical Center, University of Hiawatha, Hiawatha, Hi.

15. On a grant from Glass Bottles Inc.

16. Former technician, British Egg Marketing Board.

in a difficult field. Dr Ed Li Yi, criticising egg counts, urged that one must look someplace else for the perfect end-point. Dr Jay Jerome thought we should be much wiser if we knew what was going on in the doggone ovaries. He suspected that all the follicles had gotten shot to heck. Dr Irving Katz guessed so too.

In reply, Dr Quabe thanked the speakers for their interesting comments. Concerning the metabolism of HNYWP there was a good deal of monkey business we still had to get to the bottom of, and further work was proceeding with this in mind.

The Lancet, February 1962

* * * *

There is something of the old-fashioned craftsman about an engine driver. Where skill, pluck, patience and a stout heart were concerned, Old Duffy had more than his share. He had been retired for over twenty years, but it was easy to picture him proudly rolling his train into St Pancras with the sweat and grime of the miles on his face. And now here he was, legless and lonely, in the sepulchral atmosphere of an old men's home; forgotten the glory of the footplate.

But twice he almost came back into his own. The first occasion arose during a national crisis – one of those lightning strikes which paralyse a great country in a matter of hours. Tracks lay idle, engines stood still, stations were deserted. Duffy suddenly found himself the centre of attraction. As so often happens, the cause of the dispute was obscure, and so to Duffy's bedside the old men flocked. He knew all about it. He alone could tell of what went on behind the scenes, on the rolling stock and in the depots, albeit twenty years ago.

But to the old men time stood still. After all, steam engines were the same, weren't they? And Duffy was 'in the know'. Duffy had the real inside information.

'It's them firemen,' he asserted authoritatively, between pipe puffs. 'Never nothing but trouble with them, is what I say!' And his opinion was greatly respected as long as the strike lasted.

'Give me some legs to my body, and I'd soon show them what's what,' he repeated again and again. This was no idle boast; but Duffy's working days were over.

It had begun only a few weeks before he retired. At first only one toe turned black. The surgeons did their best but the struggle was unequal. They took off his toe, then the foot, then the leg. Duffy was not one to give in easily. A week after the third operation he was hopping on his crutches as if nothing had happened and the surgeons were delighted.

'We'll give you a shiny new leg which will never go bad, and make a new man of you,' they promised him.

But old Duffy was unsure. 'When I had both legs,' he argued, 'one of them went bad. Like as not, two legs don't agree with me anymore. So if I go walking two-legged like, it'll happen again, is what I say.'

It took them a long time to persuade him, for he could be as stubborn as a mule and no sooner thought of going back on his views than of budging beyond a closed train signal. For two years he hopped about happily with his crutches before finally giving in to reason. He had scarcely mastered his artificial leg when the toes of his remaining foot turned black. When the leg was amputated, he uttered not one word of reproach.

The subject of two artificial limbs was not broached for some time and then only to meet with impenetrable resistance. Logic and persuasion were useless, for always came his final words: 'I know what I know, and that's all there's to it.'

Meanwhile, he taught himself to jump on and off his bed from his wheelchair, and because he seemed contented enough and because he was old, he was allowed to go his own way.

Then Duffy's grandchildren reached the age when a steam engine holds more fascination than the world itself.

'Take us to see the trains,' they begged repeatedly.

At last he could bear it no longer. The second leg was fitted and the long struggle to master two artificial limbs began. Progress was slow, but once again Duffy became the centre of attraction. From their beds and from their wheelchairs, the old men applauded his efforts and were generous with their counsel. Day by day his paces grew bolder, his stance firmer and his spirits soared. Then, one fine Sunday, in full view of the admiring glances of his friends, visitors and staff, he strutted proudly once round the garden. But for the oppression in his chest, he might have gone round a second time,

In his way, of course, Duffy was right. His body was like an engine – rust in one place, rust all over. He was not meant to walk on two legs anymore. You cannot drive a bad engine. Nature, like trains, must run to schedule.

But those who saw Duffy's last walk know it was a great achievement.

The Lancet, July 1962

Lecture given to 2nd European Congress of Perinatal Medicine
10th April 1970
A Mobile Neonatal Care Unit

As you drove into London from Heathrow, some of you may have noticed a massive new building going up between Hammersmith and Fulham. This will become the new Charing Cross Hospital – conceived more than twenty years ago and now at last approaching term. It is only right and proper that the paediatric department, and especially our neonatal intensive care unit, should have been rehoused in a temporary building on this site – prematurely.

Meanwhile, our two obstetric departments are situated in Central and North London, about ten to fifteen kilometres away. I cannot help feeling that if nature had intended obstetricians and paediatricians to work fifteen kilometres apart, man would have been given an umbilical cord longer than thirty-five centimetres.[17]

There will always be a demand for moving some newborn infants to a specialised unit. It is obviously impossible to provide the facilities for neonatal intensive care in all hospitals where babies are born. In fact, about 30% of the babies sent to us are born in maternity units outside our group. Therefore the transfer of babies requiring special care is not peculiar to the Charing Cross Group.

I really must pay tribute to the excellent work done by the regular ambulance services, especially the speed – often verging

---

17. Dad rarely included jokes in his lectures and was certainly no *bon vivant*. So he was surprised, and I think quite chuffed, that the audience enjoyed this joke. He had to wait two or three minutes for the laughter to die down before continuing his speech.

on heroism – with which drivers rush ill babies to hospital. I am sure we have all seen the dramatic arrival of a cold, blue, collapsed and possibly apnoeic[18] baby inside a Perspex coffin, accompanied by a young, frightened and untrained nurse.

In trying to overcome the problem, it was clear that we should have to collect sick babies ourselves, and to collect them in such a way that treatment would begin with the arrival of our team – in other words, a special care unit on wheels. Something that could hasten to an ill baby and make possible, if need be, full emergency treatment from the moment of arrival so that the return journey can be elective, unhurried and free from hazard.

Thanks to the generosity of the Variety Club, a specially designed purpose-built mobile baby care unit was presented to us in May 1968. Oxygen is piped from three large cylinders at the front of the vehicle. The supply is adequate for two hours of really high continuous use. There is a fitted resuscitation trolley containing emergency equipment, sterile packs and a respirator. An intensive care incubator is installed in the ambulance. This contains a battery and charger which automatically switches to battery operation when the mains supply is interrupted. When the ambulance is stationary, it will normally be plugged into a mains supply by means of a long extension cable. And this ensures not only a warm incubator, but also a charged battery, a pre-warmed engine and the luxury of hot water.

In our first fifteen months' experience with the ambulance, 147 babies were carried on 137 journeys. None died on the journey but thirty-five died later. In fact, altogether so far, we have had only one death on a journey – this was an infant with extensive bilateral ventricular haemorrhages and a temperature of thirty degrees centigrade.

---

18. No longer breathing.

Our longest distance was thirty-five kilometres. There is really only one limiting factor and that is the length of time we can spare trained staff to be away from the department. On receipt of a call, our first step is to contact the first available driver on a roster. And I should explain here that our ambulance is driven by off-duty police drivers on a voluntary basis. Our average journey time is only thirty minutes, but the average total time taken from the receipt of a call to the admission of the baby to the ambulance is seventy-three minutes. The time taken for our team to arrive compares favourably with the time it takes to bring a baby in by regular ambulance, but it is still far too long. I am glad to say that on four occasions it was possible for our ambulance to arrive in time for a delivery at risk. This is of course the ideal we should like to attain much more often.

We obviously believe in giving oxygen liberally on the journey. Eight babies were brought in on intermittent positive pressure with one lone survivor. Since this survey, we have had two more survivors after (intermittent positive pressure) ventilation on the journey – one a hydrops and the other pneumonia.

Hypothermia is still our biggest enemy. In spite of a heated incubator in a heated ambulance, a heat shield and silver swaddlers, far too many babies arrive cold. As you might expect, the smaller and the more ill the infant, the lower the temperature. When we look into this further, we can see that in seventy babies whose temperatures were recorded before leaving the hospital of birth, many were already cold by the time our team arrived on the scene. If we look at the temperature differences between departure and arrival at Fulham, cold babies actually *gained* about half a degree centigrade on the journey and a few hot babies lost half a degree.

Our mobile unit is a prototype and the Variety Club intends to give more and better ones to other centres. Some of you here today may well be fortunate enough to receive one. I have not touched on the administrative problems of providing this kind of emergency service, but what I will say is that it has been worth it. I am confident that a vehicle especially designed for the purpose is vital if sick infants moved to a special care unit are to have the best possible chances for normal survival.

Our admissions are a selected group from a dozen hospitals over a wide area and it would be meaningless to compare our mortality with other special units. But I should like to conclude by showing you the neonatal mortality in the larger of the two maternity units in the Charing Cross Group – Kingsbury Maternity Hospital. The national average for England and Wales is 12.3 per thousand live births. At Kingsbury, the mortality fell from 9.1 in 1966 to 5.9 in 1968 when the ambulance came into service. Last year it was 5.2.

Ways of the Zodiac

'It's very provoking,' Humpty Dumpty said to Alice after a long silence, 'to be called an egg – very! With a name like yours, you might be any shape – almost.' It is curious how closely the name of a person often mirrors his image. In our special care unit at present, the smallest baby is called Smallman (a boy), and Baby Toomer has a lump on his back. The hospital photographer is Snapper, Miss Rawbone is our catering officer and Sister Long is six feet tall. A particular favourite of mine is Jeremy Sprinkler with enuresis I cannot cure.

Another favourite is Mrs Ng and her little boy. He was born by caesarean section and, owing to the alarming nature of his antenatal history, the obstetrician asked me to be present at the birth. Mrs Ng, who has even more charm than most of her countrywomen of equal rank and station, had conceived after several years of relative infertility. In accordance with custom, the stars were consulted and the predictions were unfavourable. This was accepted with the fatalistic resignation true to Buddhist doctrine, unruffled by the simple obstetric faith whereby a happy event is forecast on the 280th day after the last menstrual period. Mrs Ng was far too polite to allow the disparity between the obstetric and astrological forecasts to show. Both she and her husband, a diplomatic envoy of his country, maintained outwardly what I would come to know so well – a veneer of unfailing courtesy and charm over a Far Eastern inscrutability which is the tradition of a thousand dynasties.

In the sixth month, she reported that fetal movements had ceased and the cheery optimism of the obstetric staff became guarded. One month later, during which time there was a growing conviction that the baby was no longer alive, the fetal movements miraculously returned. But what great secret lay behind that closed wall between the obstetrician's hand and the baby? What thoughts behind the mask of inscrutability? A series of tests began – oestriol estimations, X-rays, ultrasound. The state of the baby remained an enigma. More is known of the astronaut on the surface of the moon than the well-being of the fetus *in utero*. The suspense became intolerable and taking all factors into consideration – the infertility, poor weight gain, low oestriol levels, absent movements for one month and the mother's short stature (her height was only 4' 10") – an elective caesarean section at 38 weeks was planned.

Shortly before we went into the theatre, Mr Ng approached and with the impeccable English of a foreign diplomat asked if he might witness the operation. My astonished surgical colleague refused without a moment's thought, adding soothingly that if on the next occasion his wife had a normal delivery he would be very welcome in the labour ward. Mr Ng withdrew with practised diplomacy. There may be more than one reason for a father wishing to see the birth of his own child. Not all fathers are sensitive to the emotional impact of childbirth. I guessed that Mr Ng's reason for wanting to be present was to see for himself the extent of any congenital abnormalities (as the stars had so ambiguously foretold) at the earliest opportunity. I assured him that I would tell him myself about the baby's condition as soon as possible after the birth and I thought I detected the shadow of a glimmer of understanding as it flitted across his half-closed eyes.

At the birth, the baby looked small but in good condition. He struggled vigorously as he was held upside down below the level of the mother's abdomen and gave several lusty cries when mucus was aspirated from his nose, mouth and pharynx. There is nothing more effective in deterring a newborn baby from misbehaving himself than the presence of a paediatrician – or is it that the worst disasters always seem to happen when one is far away? At one minute, with clear air passages, expanded lungs and a transfusion of some 100ml of placental blood to fill the myriad network of pulmonary arteries and veins now open for the first time, his vital signs were good enough to justify an Apgar[19] score of 10. A rapid clinical examination showed him to be perfectly normal except in two respects. He was at least six weeks premature and his umbilical cord contained only one artery instead of the normal complement of two.

The assessment of a baby's maturity is far from easy. The birth weight alone is not informative enough because at least one baby in every three of low birth weight is light for reasons other than prematurity. Some are light because they have been starved by a badly functioning placenta and others because their genetic make-up has determined their small size. Small mothers usually make small placentas and small babies. Prematurity, nutrition, inheritance and ante-natal abnormalities may all combine in a single baby to effect a low birth weight.

Baby Ng showed several unmistakeable features of prematurity. His ears contained so little formed cartilage that they could be crumpled up like tissue paper. The palms of his hands and the soles of his feet held few creases. Both testes were high and the scrotal skin had few rugae. His skull was slightly springy and its circumference only 12½ inches. Sparse lanugo hair covered his shoulders. It was

---

19. A handy scoring system to assess the condition of a newborn infant with points for heart rate, breathing, muscle tone, and so on.

possible to straighten out his legs at the knees with little force and yet he resisted any attempt to turn down his hands at the wrist or lift up his feet at the ankle, the very reverse of the findings in a term infant.

His preceding history began to fall into place. The fetal movements had been absent during the sixth month because the pregnancy was only in its fifth month. The oestriol levels and X-ray signs were all consistent with an error in the expected date of delivery. The clinical features were those of an infant of about 34 weeks' gestation. This sleeping life had been plucked from its roots before time and, like a small miracle, began in an instant to fetch and carry oxygen with unripe lungs and startled heart.

The findings of only one artery in the cord was something which would certainly have been missed only a few years ago. A good customs officer always examines closely both traveller and luggage. Paediatricians too have come to realise the need for a close inspection of the cord and placenta. Baby Ng's placenta looked outwardly normal enough and its weight, one pound, in the expected proportion of 1:4 at 34 weeks' maturity. However, the cut surface of the cord showed only two structures, an oval, thin-walled vein and a round, hard, white, protruding artery. The presence of a single artery is uncommon, occurring only once in some three hundred births. Although a single vessel can still carry all the necessary blood to the placenta – after all, only a single vessel carries it back – the absence of one of the arteries may be part of a developmental abnormality. A careful search for other congenital abnormalities, especially of the heart or kidneys, will be revealing in approximately one baby in five with a single umbilical artery. Baby Ng was obviously one of the four normal ones with this unusual feature.

How was one to explain all this to the father waiting outside? The simple way out was to say that the child was normal, but his face failed to betray the expected relief. Instead, he made yet another surprising request. Saying that he had the utmost faith in my judgement, he hoped I would grant his boy the privilege of becoming my private patient. It was written in the child's horoscope that he would not be normal, and he would feel happier if I could go back and have a second look at the baby. 'But the stars could be wrong,' I said. 'The stars do not lie,' said Mr Ng, his expression inscrutable. 'This time they must have made a mistake,' I countered. 'He should have been born under Libra and not Virgo.' I explained how and why he came to be at least one month premature and what difference this would make. His face remained calm. 'The signs in the sky are a fact,' he said patiently. 'It was written that he would be born under the sign of this month, and that is also a fact.' The logic of the argument was unassailable. No man-made intervention can change the course of destiny. I launched into a lecture on the implications of a single umbilical artery and we parted on the best of terms – he the wiser for one of the least known and least obvious of congenital abnormalities, and me the richer for a lesson in diplomacy and a glimpse of the oriental occult.

We agreed that I should see him a few times in the NHS follow-up clinic. Leaving other considerations aside, he was after all a British subject and therefore entitled to this service. I was also anxious not to miss any late complications such as a urinary tract infection. The first three weeks passed without incident and he was discharged home when he weighed just over five pounds.

His first two follow-up examinations were satisfactory and I gave him an appointment to be seen at the age of six months, but long before this time he was back with a letter from the Health Visitor. He had steadfastly resisted any attempt to make him gain at the normal rate with the result that, at four months, he weighed just under 10 pounds. Various measures from cereals to Complan had failed to make any impression on his weight chart. The letter told of problems and difficulties of communication, and hinted darkly of strange Eastern feeding customs to account for the poor weight gain.

The mystery of strange feeding practices was easy to clear up. Mrs Ng had merely tried to tempt him with *Shoa Mai* – a national dish prepared from finely shredded pork, honeyed chicken, snow peas, water-chestnut, butterfly prawns, thousand-year egg, and almonds and young bamboo shoots, all steamed to perfection in a special dish. From start to finish, it takes almost two days to make and, as I was to find out later, achieves a blend of flavours so exquisite as to entice the palate of a Philistine.

Physical examination of the baby – at this stage he still had no first name because the stars were not clear enough on this point – was normal but he was undeniably small. At birth he had measured 17 inches. Now he was only 22 inches. Baby Ng's height and weight were both below average but in the correct proportion to one another. If he had been any heavier, he would have been overweight for his size. The problem was not one of feeding but of growth. As he was not growing as fast as the average English baby of his age, his food requirements were correspondingly less.

The problem now was to determine whether his growth pattern was within the normal range or whether he was destined to become a dwarf. The problem was complicated by his estimated prematurity, the knowledge that he had been born with only one umbilical artery, and possibly the forebodings of the astrologer. The first task was to plot his measurements on a longitudinal growth chart. Assuming that he was born six weeks before the true expected date of delivery, he fell between the 3rd and 10th percentile lines for length, weight and head circumference. So far so good. At least he came within the normal range and if he continued to grow along the same path he would attain a height of about 5'4" by the age of 18 or 20 years. Such a prediction is of course never possible from only two measurements in the first four months, but it can usually be made with confidence by the age of two years.

It was not necessary to look far for a reason for his small size. His mother, dainty and petite, herself measured only 4'10" and the father's height was only 5'5". The question now arose whether the baby would be regarded at the lower limit of normal if plotted on a growth chart based on normal children from his own country. Clearly, there was no justification in expecting him to conform to the growth pattern of English and Scottish children. It seemed likely that he would come well within the normal range, and indeed my prediction that he would weigh 16 pounds at one year and 20 pounds at two turned out to be remarkably accurate. As he grew, he made up in intellect what he lacked in stature. Few are those without their weaknesses and the strengths to make up for them.

Frequently throughout the time of his follow-up, I enquired after his first name, always to be met by the same evasive, shy, secret smile and a murmured apology about the ways of the Zodiac. He was nearly two when, after I had predicted a final height of 5'4½" for him, his mother asked whether I would do her the honour of accepting an invitation to a reception at the Embassy at which her husband was the ambassador. In due course, I received a magnificently printed invitation. On the evening in question, I was picked up by the ambassador's own car and taken to the reception where Mr Ng met me in the foyer and, leading me deftly through a throng of several hundred guests, introduced me to the Prime Minister who shook me warmly by the hand. The evening passed surprisingly quickly, the guests left and I found myself one of the select few invited to join the guest of honour, here on a State Visit, in a special banquet prepared for him in another room. The *Shoa Mai* was out of this world and as the evening wore to a close, one could sense an indefinable relaxation in the inscrutability of my hosts. I turned to Mr Ng and asked whether his astrologer had yet thought up a suitable name for his little boy. 'As a matter of fact, he has,' he said in his impeccable clipped English. 'U.' I fancied I saw the ghost of a smile flutter for a moment at the corners of his eyes before dancing quickly out of sight.

Midwife and Health Visitor, 1973

Heather's Baby

Is heredity or environment the more important in the unfolding of a child's personality? The question is as old and unanswerable as that well-known conundrum about the chicken and the egg. The truth is that both have a profound influence on the formative years and there is little point in devaluating one at the expense of the other. Everybody can think of at least one anecdotal instance in which the advantage of birth or affluence conferred the stronger contribution. Inward strength may triumph over adversity and intellect may overcome social injustice. It is also possible for good fortune to smile on those who have little ability, just as cruel fate can destroy those who have much. Human heritage is more than just a few goods and chattels left after death. Embracing heredity, culture and society in a changing world, who can say which is the most powerful?

As I was glancing through the pages of a Sunday newspaper recently, my attention was suddenly arrested by the photograph of a girl. The face and features were unmistakeable. The name alone was unfamiliar. The resemblance was too striking to be mere coincidence. It brought back memories of twenty-five years ago and made me reflect on the riddle of genes and destiny.

In 1948 I was a newly qualified house physician starting my first appointment on the children's ward of my teaching hospital. The immense changes between then and now would in themselves fill a book. The ward was never empty and the waiting list unmanageable. Hours were long and off-duty non-existent. Doctors commanded immense respect but were almost powerless against the overwhelming severity and variety of illness to which children succumbed in the spring of life. The art of nursing had reached heights unequalled today.

I can still remember Heather clearly. A delightful 9-year-old, she had been admitted with severe abdominal pain followed by joint pains and a rash. She had anaphylactoid purpura, also known as Henoch-Schönlein disease. Clinical diagnosis was often easy in those days, but investigations were limited and treatment was largely empirical. Even today, the cause of this condition is uncertain but, as in rheumatic fever, it seems likely that it is an unusual type of allergic reaction to a streptococcal infection.

Heather was ill for about a month, during which time we often debated whether or not to look inside her pain-racked tummy in case our diagnosis was wrong. Curiously enough, the deciding factor to which we always returned concerned her glamorous mother and the importance of avoiding an abdominal scar as far as possible. Her mother's name was Fay and she was a star of stage, screen and radio at the height of her popularity. Heather's father was also a well-known actor and it was understood that she would follow in her parents' footsteps.

The life of a house-physician held few rewards and Fay's visits became the highlight of the day. I never lost an opportunity on checking various details of the history over and over again, and even the medical students became conspicuous by their presence. The ward was her stage and she made her entrances and exits as superbly. She was grateful and was determined to repay us in the way she knew best. She brought all the glitter and glamour of stardom to a drab ward of unhappy children and work-weary staff as if no other audience mattered. As soon as she appeared, the children would chorus from all corners of the ward: 'I want Heather's mummy to read to me.' Some could scarcely raise their voices above a whisper. Most touching of all was a little girl with a tracheostomy who, poking a small finger over the opening, added her half-choked plea to the others. And to hear Fay read a children's story was an entrancing experience.

Heather recovered and went home. The ward was once again sad and the little girl with the tracheostomy died. Seven years went by and I was a registrar in a newly built premature baby unit at another hospital. The science of neonatal care was awakening. We had incubators, antibiotics, exchange transfusions and oxygen. (Too much oxygen.) We had suddenly become aware of a hitherto unrecognised scourge of prematurity – hyaline membrane disease. Soon after birth, babies grunted and panted, their sternums bowing inwards with each breath. The lucky ones came through after two or three days; the others fought for life to the point of exhaustion, apnoea[20] and cyanosis.[21] The standard treatment consisted of oxygen, selfless nursing and masterly inactivity; intensive supportive care was yet to come. We were sent babies by maternity hospitals and nursing homes from all over London, and one day we were sent Heather's baby.

The baby, a girl, weighed three pounds and was eight weeks premature. She had been born by caesarean section. (I saw a child's abdomen and the scar that would now be written upon it forever.) Already there was severe respiratory distress. Heather, who could have been little more than 16 years of age, was unmarried. Her parents had been filming in America and she had managed to keep it secret from them. They were due to return in a few days and Heather was determined that they should never find out. Already a starlet in her own right, she used her considerable charms to

---

20. No longer breathing.
21. A blue tinge to the skin caused by lack of oxygen.

persuade an obstetrician to perform an elective section a few days before their return and to be a party to the subterfuge by giving out that she had had an appendicectomy.

Her parents hurried to her bedside as soon as they had received the telegram she had so deceitfully composed before she went into the nursing home. She had no wish to keep or even see the baby. Indeed, as it turned out, she had made arrangements for the baby to be fostered. Presumably it had been explained to her that the chances of survival after a caesarean section at 32 weeks were less than one in ten. This was 1955. Even today, a mortality of about 50% must be anticipated. But Heather did not care about the outcome either way. I think she might have been dismayed to know that the baby had come under my care, but her private affairs were not my concern and her secret remained safe.

This time, regretfully, there were to be no visits from Fay. All we had was a breathless baby struggling for survival and on her puckered premature face the unmistakeable features of Fay and Heather. For a week she fought the fight of her life. Luckily, those early incubators were leaky and inefficient. It was impossible to raise the oxygen concentration high enough even had we wanted to. Thus, through sheer good fortune she escaped blindness from the excessive use of oxygen – a condition known as retrolental fibroplasia[22] which had become one of the most common and mysterious complications in the best premature baby units.

She became deeply jaundiced. We had only just become

---

22. Abnormal proliferation of blood vessels immediately behind the lens of the eye which then leak or bleed, causing scarring to the retina. It affected many premature babies in the 1950s, owing to the excessive administration of oxygen. Now called retinopathy of prematurity, it affects around 20% of babies who are born prematurely. It mainly occurs in babies who are born before week thirty-two of pregnancy or weigh less than 1,500g when they are born.

aware of the injurious effects of a high bilirubin level. At last it lay within our power to prevent one form of brain damage. On the fourth day, I performed an exchange transfusion to the accompaniment of attacks of cyanosis, apnoea and bradycardia.[23] The procedure took over three hours as I alternately withdrew and injected only 5ml amounts of blood. Once again, our luck held. The new blood seemed to possess some factor – perhaps it was glucose – missing in her own, and after the transfusion her condition was much better.

There was one more factor which contributed to her successful recovery – probably the most important of them all. The Sister of the Unit had a rare and remarkable gift for looking after premature babies. The more ill they were, the more she could rise to the occasion. This baby presented her with an irresistible challenge. For all of seven days and nights, she did not leave the side of that incubator for more than two hours. What little rest she grudgingly allowed herself she had in her small office on the ward. No other nurse was permitted to handle this baby. She did not spare herself – she did everything herself. For the whole of the first crucial weeks, those remarkable green fingers kindled a flickering flame into full life.

I was curious to see Heather and her mother again, but I decided it was better to let matters rest. Also, there was the intriguing distraction of Mrs A. The day Heather's baby was admitted, a woman in her mid-thirties appeared at the door, introduced herself as Mrs A and asked whether she might visit the baby from time to time. Little did we guess how involved she was to become, even to the extent of sleeping in the hospital when the baby's condition was at its most serious. Mrs A was Heather's pre-arranged foster-mother.

---

23. Slowing of the pulse.

The gradual growth of a curious symbiosis between this stranger, in whose sad, dark eyes lay written the tragedy of her race, and our Sister, whose starchy, forbidding exterior concealed a cruelly-deprived maternal instinct, was fascinating to watch. Both shared the same desperate need, both were exhausted by the long vigil, both wanted the same baby. One stood by helplessly while the other coaxed life and strength into frail limbs; soon, their roles would be reversed. The child would be carried out and away in strange arms. The relationship which unfolded became a kaleidoscope of conflict and common sympathy, of rivalry, jealousy, strength and weakness, and of mutual understanding.

Gradually Mrs A was accepted. With infinite patience, she sat hour after hour waiting for news, for a sign, for anything – indeed we knew not what. In retrospect, her actions are more understandable. She herself had had no children after twelve years of marriage and had been told that it would be quite impossible for her to conceive. She was the barren partner in a marriage which could not survive childlessness. Adoption, the obvious answer, was surprisingly difficult. The Church adoption societies would not agree to help her. The Children's Department of the Local Authority did not assist with adoptions. The Local Authority of the neighbouring district did, but refused to help her because she did not live in the area and also on account of her European extraction. Private third-party adoption was the only recourse left. Twice she had almost adopted a child. The first had a congenital malformation of the heart, of which she knew nothing until she found the baby dead in its cot only a few days after she brought him home. The second, also a boy, was a bouncing toddler when the mother, who had repeatedly absconded before every court hearing, eventually decided that she had changed her mind and would give him to relatives instead. This was the most bitter hurt of all.

Our Sister believed in early feeding. She could well afford to because she alone had the gift of being able to feed small babies without serious risk of regurgitation and subsequent inhalation. She also had an unshakeable faith in breast milk, so much so that we bought it daily all the way from Cardiff. On the second day, we were desperately busy and there was no-one who could be spared to meet the 7:22am train at Paddington the following morning. 'Please let me go,' pleaded Mrs A. Ungraciously, Sister agreed – there was no alternative – and collecting the milk from Paddington each morning became the first of her regular tasks. She could not have been more overjoyed had she been able to give the milk from her own breast. At last she was able to do something positive in order that she might share in the baby's recovery. Soon she sewed mittens, rolled bandages, folded gauze squares and performed numerous other tasks, each new one bringing the inner satisfaction which comes from giving without reward. Is this not what childbirth is about? *In sorrow thou shalt bring children forth.*

The baby was almost three months old when, dressed in the most expensive clothes we had seen for a long time, Mrs A took her home. She had not been christened and instead had acquired the hybrid of Feather which neatly described the genealogy, the birth weight and the balance in which her life had hung in the first weeks. Anticipating a painful parting, Mrs A had thoughtfully given Sister a pair of delicate gold ear-rings, touching on a femininity which had no cause to lie dormant, and a framed photograph of Feather. It was this photograph and its background which now seemed to gaze back serenely from the pages of my Sunday newspaper.

The arrangement for Feather's follow-up was that she

would be seen regularly by a doctor friend of the family, and we never saw her again. Sixteen years is a long time but the face was unmistakeably that of Heather and Fay. The paper had its usual quota of aspiring young actresses in model-like pose, over-eager to catch the camera-man's eyes, but this picture immediately stood out from among the others. It was more than just the usual fun-loving teenager hoping to be spotted by a film scout. The same formula of the pretty face, short skirt and long legs was there, but there was a book on her lap and she was surrounded by a group of obviously blind children, some of whom had stretched out their hands to touch her.

'Naomi A,' read the description, 'is a 16-year-old schoolgirl with a difference. She spends all her spare time reading to children who cannot see, bringing in the sunshine to the Sunshine Homes. She believes there is nothing worse than being born blind and she hopes one day to become an eye surgeon.'

Naomi A. Even the name was purpose-built for a life of play-acting. Presumably Mrs A eventually had adopted her legally. An idea suddenly occurred to me. The thought of an elective section at 32 weeks for no better reason than to save a family scandal had always nagged me. I reached for my *Medical Directory* and quickly turned the pages until I found A. The name itself was an unusual one, the coincidence far too great to be credible. The entry described A as an obstetrician and gynaecologist. It gave the usual degrees and diplomas, followed by a list of the hospitals at which he worked. Sure enough, one of these was the nursing home where Heather had given birth to her baby.

Midwife and Health Visitor, 1974

An Act of God

It always seems strange to me that the worst disaster to befall one should be called an 'act of God'. Life is but a lucky accident. It would be so much more in keeping with the spirit of the Creation to attribute life rather than death to divine intervention. Birth is a miracle matched only by the growth of a child, unfolding at last to the fulfilment of parenthood. The thread is delicate and ever fragile, held intact by staying hands on the spinning wheel of fortune. The continuity of this slender thread is a provident miracle.

The Grants were the sort of couple who knew what it meant for the thread to break, not once but four times. After three miscarriages, Mrs Grant had a Shirodkar[24] suture inserted around the cervix and was rested for the greater part of the fourth pregnancy only to develop severe pre-eclampsia. At last, with a soaring blood pressure despite bed rest and sedation, the stitch was removed at the thirtieth week. She went into labour almost immediately, giving birth to a stillborn baby boy. For a time, her fifth pregnancy looked like following the same pattern. Her blood pressure began to climb once more after the twenty-fifth week, and four weeks later a premature delivery could no longer be avoided if her own life was to be saved.

Intensive preparations were made for the resuscitation of the baby and the subsequent care in the special care unit. Off-duty arrangements were altered, equipment was checked, oxygen cylinders were filled, an incubator was switched on a full day in advance and a full-scale dress-rehearsal was performed. As the laryngoscope was snapped

---

24. A stitch around the neck of the womb to allow the pregnancy to continue.

open, the light glowed brightly, then suddenly flickered and went out. The batteries were quickly changed but no light returned. A frantic search for a spare bulb followed and it was almost twenty minutes before a replacement could be found. The experience proved that a spare bulb and batteries were essential items on the resuscitation tray. 'Why not have two laryngoscopes?' one of the house officers suggested. Why not indeed, and a second laryngoscope was added for good measure.

Their daughter was born weighing all of two pounds and two ounces, with a strong heartbeat but severely depressed. I immediately prepared to intubate her. As I snapped the laryngoscope open, the light glowed momentarily, flickered and went out. I snatched the second laryngoscope from the tray and, seconds later, the tube was in place and her chest was moving gently in time to the steady, rhythmical insufflations of oxygen. The respirator served us well. Three days later, she breathed without help; three months later, she went home; three years later, she was a fine bonny girl and normal in every way.

Of course, this is a considerable over-simplification of everything else that was done for her – treatment summed up modestly by the term 'intensive care'. What matters most is that she grew into a lively and attractive toddler who, as each new day dawned, proved over and over again that the saying 'Two's company, three's none' is simply just not true. Alison became the chain and anchor of a marriage which could never have survived childlessness. Both her parents worshipped her to distraction. This, their faith, united them with a force that nothing could tear asunder. She completed a bond of interdependence so powerful that the terrible thought of anything untoward ever happening to her was too hard to contemplate. The three of them were inseparable and it was particularly touching to hear about their outings and holidays together.

One year they went to Spain. We discussed all the usual precautions about travel, immunisation, vaccination and food poisoning. They hired a villa for a month. They had a magnificent time and there were no medical mishaps except for Mr Grant who got a speck of sand in his eye when he allowed himself to be buried up to the neck for the sake of a little general amusement.

It was during an English sea-side holiday two years later that Alison suddenly fell ill. She became listless and feverish and soon her temperature began to swing alarmingly in the region of 105 degrees Fahrenheit. A local doctor was called in and when he was baffled, he arranged for her admission to the local hospital – and, as it happens, a very good one.

The parents were told that she had an infection and a few days should suffice to discover its cause and to bring about its cure. She remained well in herself and the usual investigations were quickly put under way. Microscopy and culture of a mid-stream specimen of urine was perfectly clear – a very disappointing finding since a urinary tract infection headed the list of provisional diagnoses. A chest X-ray was clear, ruling out a chest infection. A throat swab yielded nothing other than the normal kind of organism. A stool culture was also free from pathogenic bacteria.

She developed a fleeting rash, sometimes there and sometimes not. Perhaps she had one of the common childhood viral infectious fevers. More swabs and some serum were sent to the laboratory. Virological studies invariably take several weeks, the results arriving long after the clinical situation has resolved itself. However, a few days would soon show whether her symptoms and signs conformed to the known childhood fevers. When those days were up, it was clear she did not have one of the common viral infections and, indeed, months later the results of swab and serum tests were negative.

A week of high swinging pyrexia began to make her look toxic. Her parents and specialists became alarmed and the search for a diagnosis was intensified. Other doctors were called in, each one suggesting yet another test. Her white blood count showed a surprising deficiency of cells, especially of the neutrophil series. The red cell sedimentation rate was fantastically high, proving that 'something was going on'. There was no evidence of glandular fever and the specific blood test for this common, benign infection of young people – the Paul Bunnell test – was negative.

By now, the child was beginning to look really ill. She had a hectic flush and had clearly lost weight. Her spleen had become impressively enlarged and she complained of pains in her joints and abdomen. Normally a co-operative, happy, outgoing little girl, she now showed all the outward signs of distress of illness, separation from her parents, hospitalisation and the battery of blood tests she had had to endure.

One of the adult physicians had seen a similar illness in a patient with typhoid septicaemia. Another suggested the possibility of tuberculosis. Brucellosis and toxoplasmosis would also have to be excluded. A series of blood cultures at the height of the fever might demonstrate the cause. It would be wise to start again at the beginning, repeating some of the tests to which one negative answer had already been obtained. More tests, more blood, more pain. The results all came back – negative.

The disease was now in its third week and the parents were frantic. It was decided to start some kind of empirical treatment. But what? A conference of all those involved was called. The paediatrician and the bacteriologist were in favour of giving a broad-spectrum antibiotic. The rheumatologist thought she might be an atypical case of Still's disease – a childhood variant of rheumatoid arthritis – and that she should have a course of steroids. The haematologist pointed out that this would mask the features of leukaemia and that a bone marrow puncture should be performed before any steroid drug was given. The inevitable compromise was reached – she was to receive all three. A bone marrow aspiration was done (and reported as normal), and a course of an antibiotic and a steroid were ordered.

The effect of the treatment was disappointing. Her fever continued unabated, her wasting was now pitiful to behold and the high flush on her cheeks had been replaced by an earthy pallor. Perhaps the doses were not high enough. Perhaps the wrong antibiotic had been chosen. Perhaps injections would be more effective than oral drugs. She was sinking fast, perhaps already beyond caring whether she had injections or not. Four-hourly injections were ordered.

Once again the effect was disappointing, although not without revealing yet another dramatic manifestation of the disease. At each injection site, she developed a large, unsightly bruise. A platelet count showed that, like the decrease in white blood cells, the number of platelets was also seriously deficient. A catastrophic haemorrhage could occur at any moment. Already, the nurses had difficulty in stemming the trickles of blood following every injection. Soon she was covered in huge bruises, blood appeared in the urine and she had several terrifying nosebleeds. Her haemoglobin level fell precipitously and the first of several emergency blood transfusions was given.

At this point, the parents decided to make one final and desperate bid for her life. They decided to come home. Home meant staying together to the bitter end. Home also meant returning to the hospital where she had been born and had miraculously survived. Here the thin thread of life had held fast against impossible odds once before. If only...

She was hardly in a fit state to move two hundred miles, but such was their distress that no-one could bring himself to dissuade them. They asked for nothing except to take their one and only child, reduced to little more than a thin, white bundle of skin and bone, into their car and drive the long drive back to London. The father drove non-stop like someone possessed, while the child gradually sank into coma as she lay cradled in her mother's arms and the sands of time steadily ran out.

I saw her as soon as she arrived. The other hospital had thoughtfully allowed all her records, investigations, X-rays and charts to accompany her. On examination, her appearance exceeded all my worst fears. She was barely conscious and blood trickled from almost every orifice. She was covered from head to toe in large bruises and not one vein could be seen that was not already surrounded by extravasated blood. She was grossly anaemic and in heart failure. The liver and spleen were very large and stood out grotesquely beneath the skeleton and her wasted abdomen. And her temperature was 105 degrees Fahrenheit.

The clinical picture was that of terminal leukaemia, very likely in its last two or three days. The earlier marrow examination must be wrong. There must have been some mistake in the area from which it had been taken, or perhaps even in its interpretation. And yet, I could not bring myself to tell her parents what I thought. Their eyes alone were eloquent, no words passed their lips. 'Where there is life there is hope,' I told them, and we set about resuscitating her. With unbelievable good fortune, we found a tiny vein – a lifeline for a fresh blood transfusion and drugs to support the heart. We placed her in oxygen. And we ordered a repeat marrow examination. 'Would it wait until tomorrow?' I was asked. 'The Senior Haematologist is retiring today, and there is to be a farewell party with many guests and a presentation.' I said no. It occurred to me that if he was leaving, it was all the more important to obtain his opinion right away.

The sample was withdrawn without difficulty and she was far too ill to feel any more pain. In the laboratory, a hubbub of excited disorganisation reigned. The staff and local practitioners had contributed to present him with a large framed oil-painting and were anxious to get him out of the way so that it could be smuggled into the building. I caught him just as he was about to be taken out for the remainder of the afternoon. As everyone else appeared to be busy preparing for his farewell, he locked himself in his little room that in one hour he would be leaving for good, and started to fix and stain the slides himself. He was left alone; there were no telephone calls and no interruptions.

Suddenly an excited shout brought most of the hospital staff hurriedly to his microscope. There, brilliantly stained and magnified, lay hundreds of small, pale, blue ovoid cells between the scant normal cells of human bone marrow. As the slide moved and a new field came into the light of the microscope, more and still more of these invading cells were revealed. The marrow teemed with them. 'These,' he said with the authority of forty years' experience, 'are the classical parasites of Kala-Azar.'

There was not a moment to lose. Kala-Azar, or Leishmaniasis, is a protozoal disease which, like its distant cousin malaria, is treatable. But what treatment? I picked up the telephone and rang the Hospital for Tropical Diseases. 'I am afraid everyone has gone home,' a cultured voice answered. 'I am the only one left and I am off to South America tomorrow. Can I do anything to help?' He turned out to be the Senior Physician and an international authority on this very disease. In less than an hour, he was in my ward, looking at Alison and prescribing her treatment, the first dose of which he had thoughtfully brought with him. He told the parents not to worry, she would be completely well in a few weeks. They broke down and failed to hear the rest. The parasite would be eradicated for all time. She had the Mediterranean form; it is common in Spain and Malta. The incubation period is long and can run into years – even ten years is possible. They were in Spain two years ago and this length of time is nothing out of the ordinary. The disease is spread by a sand-fly via foxes, squirrels or stray dogs – just the sort of thing you find in a nice secluded villa with a sandy beach in front and a wood behind. It always seems to go for little children and not grown-ups, but that's the way of all parasites in this world.

To cut a long story short, Alison made her predicted recovery. To see her little body once more fill out and her delightful personality emerge from the ghastly nightmare of the previous eight weeks was a miracle in itself. Maybe the whole tenuous sequence of events should rightfully be called an Act of God.

Midwife and Health Visitor, 1975

Lactose Malabsorption

Winston Churchill once said that there could be no finer investment for any community than to put milk into babies. History proved him right but *tempora mutantur nos et mutamur in illis* (times change and we change with them). Populations have shifted, grown and emerged. There have always been people who could not or would not drink milk. Somehow there seem to be many more now, if the staggering total of 30 million lactose malabsorbers in the United States alone is anything to go by. The unpalatable truth for Western countries economically dependent on their dairy industries, and for world relief organisations, is that milk is no longer the nutritionists' universal panacea. This is the conclusion of a scholarly review by Simoons and colleagues on the geographical implications of lactose malabsorption and milk-drinking.

The disadvantages of milk-drinking range from galactosaemia, which is exceedingly rare, to cardiovascular degenerative disease, which is distressingly common; and they include milk allergy and lactose malabsorption. For practical purposes, allergy to cow's milk still defies incontrovertible means of identification, but impairment of lactose absorption lends itself to well-established diagnostic criteria, such as the measured lactase activity in a small intestine biopsy, a negligible rise in blood glucose following a lactose load of 2 g/kg, or simply the finding of a reducing sugar and a low pH in the stools. Lactose malabsorption is not necessarily synonymous with lactose or milk intolerance, since not all individuals who cannot absorb lactose properly develop symptoms if they drink milk in moderation, while there are sufferers who can be shown to absorb lactose normally.

The world can be divided roughly into the parts where people drink milk and those where they don't. Thus, based on sound diagnostic criteria, the incidence of lactose malabsorption in the native peoples of Asia, Africa, North and South America and Australia has ranged from 60 to 100 per cent of the groups studied. This contrasts sharply with an over-all incidence of around 10 per cent in Europeans and of nearly 0 per cent in Danes. If, indeed, the greater part of the world suffers from a built-in inability to absorb lactose, how have these people managed to survive until now, when human milk contains even more lactose than cow's milk? The explanation given is that babies dependent on breast-milk make enough intestinal lactase, and genetically low levels do not develop until after the first year. Thus, 'adult' lactose malabsorption begins at two to seven years!

Babies may thrive at the breast for a year or two but cannot do so indefinitely because lactase deficiency, even when it is hastened by famine and disease, is not reversible in those in whom it is destined to become the normal adult state. To give the deprived children of Africa, Asia and America milk to drink is to provide them with yet one more reason for chronic childhood diarrhoea. The evidence reviewed by Simoons and colleagues is certainly impressive. Abdominal distension, colic, diarrhoea and vomiting occur predictably in a high percentage of lactase-deficient adults and children. The groups studied include Chippewa Indians, Mexican Americans, Baltimore blacks, Peruvians and Ghanaians. The occurrence of symptoms, not unexpectedly, is in part related to the dose, so that many lactose malabsorbers can tolerate small loads, and the other constituents of milk sometimes reduce the symptoms.

Nevertheless, the question arises whether it is right to go on promoting the consumption of milk in countries and populations where absorption and tolerance are low and the nutritional state of individuals may be still further compromised. Gifts of dried milk are not always well received. In Jamaica and the Lebanon, mothers insisted that it gave their children diarrhoea; certain Navajo Indians in Arizona and New Mexico fed it to lambs instead, while in Guatemala it was sometimes used for whitewashing houses. Most of the world's milk is produced in Europe, North America, Australia and New Zealand. The interests of the milk-poor nations are not necessarily best served by importing milk or embarking on ambitious programmes of home milk production. At present powdered milk is one of the cheapest available foods, but it may make sounder long-term economic sense for the milk-poor, non-milk-drinking nations of the world to use their land for growing food for themselves rather than for animals and drinking the animals' milk.

Developmental Medicine & Child Neurology, May 1977

Letter from Abroad
Malpractice Suits in England

London – A singular piece of good fortune came my way many years ago when I won a £50 surgical prize in my final undergraduate year. I spent half this windfall on a dinner jacket and the other half on a life membership of the Medical Defence Union. Both have proved excellent investments. Imagine – total malpractice insurance for life for the incredible once-for-all payment of £30 (around $75 at the time). It is small wonder that our medicolegal insurance agencies boast they are the envy of the world even if their once indiscreet offer of life membership is now as extinct as the dodo. It is true that we have yet to suffer a US litigation explosion. In our characteristic preparedness, premiums have grown from £5 to £40 yearly (around $70), with much grouching and grumbling from my colleagues although the sum in question still stands as a monument of British modesty and understatement.[25]

I attended Court recently as an expert witness. The scene inside the impressive Royal Courts of Law in The Strand would already be familiar to devotees of Gilbert and Sullivan light opera. Counsel (my learned friends), ushers (silence in court!), clerks (place this book in your right hand and repeat after me), and beadles bustled about ceaselessly in their wigs, gowns, and gaiters, while the elitist red-robed judges (M'Lud, for short) were accorded all enviable deference. Here and there little huddles of defendants and plaintiffs went over their last-minute evidence anxiously. Several bewigged young barristers hurried by, muttering

---

25. A busy paediatrician working in both the NHS and private sector would today pay around £8,000 annually.

something about an injunction and briskly rubbing their hands with glee, like medical students off to a particularly good post-mortem. Two fresh-faced barristers-to-be in brand new wigs and gowns laughed uproariously at a legal joke in which the jury was discharged after an eight-week trial and the whole case had to be heard again from the beginning.

Our case concerned an 11-year-old boy with kernicterus.[26] His parents, immigrants from Trinidad, claimed that the condition, being preventable, should have been prevented. Therefore, as he is now badly handicapped, the hospital is to blame for not taking proper care of him. By a strange coincidence, a similar claim in another case of kernicterus, the first ever to come before a British court, had succeeded only a few days earlier, the child being awarded £16,000 for 'loss of amenity'.

The wheels of justice grind slowly. Ten years had gone by in finding a willing firm of solicitors, obtaining free legal aid, and preparing a case against the Hospital Authority. The hearing itself lasted two weeks and judgement, a whole morning. Two eminent QCs led for their clients, each supported by two juniors who took copious notes in longhand, as did the two solicitors, the clerks, the reporters, and the judge himself. At one point, I counted 15 people all taking down the proceedings in longhand. Beside the witness box, a pile of Testaments, Talmuds, Korans and *Tipiṭakas*, and even a spare yarmulke stood in anticipation for every conceivable contingency.

The sad story began just before Christmas in 1965. Born in a large National Health Service district hospital, the infant was recorded as looking jaundiced ('deeply' according to

---

26. Brain damage in babies with severe jaundice caused by dangerously high levels of bilirubin.

the nursing staff), but the physicians were unimpressed and the bilirubin level was not measured. He was discharged home on Christmas Eve, three days later. On Dec 27, he returned critically ill and with a serum bilirubin level of 57mg/100ml, only to be saved by the heroic efforts of the junior physicians for a life of irreversible, silent infancy.

The crucial issue was whether he was well enough to go home on the day that he did. His mother maintained that he was deeply jaundiced and it distressed her to take him home. The paediatrician and the ward sister, neither of whom could remember any specific details of the infant at the time, maintained that he could not have been jaundiced, because, if he had been, he would not have been sent home and that was the system. The scanty medical records signified not that the baby had been neglected but that nothing worthy of note had taken place, and that was the system.

As often happens, the main issue became clouded by many side issues. The Christmas holiday was imminent, staff was short, and presumably the few who remained on duty were busy putting up the decorations. Most mothers were probably eager to go home. Public holidays are notoriously bad times for those in need of medical attention. Patients would be reluctant to call their physicians and physicians would be reluctant to make calls. December is not a good month for detecting and assessing jaundice. The ward was on the ground floor of an old Victorian building and lighting conditions must have been less than ideal. Moreover, the child's skin was black. His routine cord blood Coomb's test was negative, so there was no obvious reason why he should become jaundiced after the sixth day. When the ward sister wrote 'deeply' in the notes she did not mean profoundly, intensely, or severely, but 'obviously'. It meant that she could see the jaundice and the mother could see the jaundice, but, no degree being implied, the physicians could be forgiven for considering it within physiological limits – a question of semantics, but that, too, was the system.

When I arrived on the scene eight years later, I found that he had a severe degree of glucose-6-phosphate dehydrogenase (G6PD) deficiency. A lengthy argument followed about the relevance of this to his neonatal illness. Did he sustain a haemolytic crisis in the three-day interval between leaving the hospital and coming back with kernicterus? Or was he jaundiced all along? What might his bilirubin level have been on Christmas Eve if it had been measured, knowing that it was 57mg/100ml only three days later? How much of that jaundice was obstructive and how much haemolytic, bearing in mind that he suffered severe and irreversible brain damage?

In defence, it was claimed on behalf of the hospital that no other case of kernicterus had occurred in 20 years – as, indeed, had no other case of G6PD deficiency (knowingly). It was unfortunate that the circumstances leading up to this one occurrence, which should have been unforgettable, had been forgotten. However, the ward sister – now a senior nursing officer – painted a harrowing picture of a typical NHS hospital in the 1960s. As sole head nurse, she was responsible for 30 mothers and 30 infants. She kept the charts, checked treatments, answered telephones, accompanied physicians on their visits and the matron on hers, supervised the orderlies in the kitchen and sluices, taught her nurses, and looked after her patients. More than 1,000 mothers and infants passed through her hands in a year. The house officer for the ward was on leave. His work was covered by the obstetric resident – there was only one – who, with 50 deliveries weekly and huge antenatal clinics, had little time for normal infants, let alone writing notes about them. The consultant paediatrician visited the obstetric block once a week. Even if he spent only three minutes by each cot, the round would take him at least two and a half hours. It was hardly likely that the doctors might discover something to which the ward sister had not already alerted them. She went on rounds to all her patients at 8am and 8pm to make sure all was well, and on the day of the consultant's round she would go round an hour early to make doubly sure. That was the system.

The medical evidence hinged heavily on published work from the United States and from Greece. The defence leaned on the much-quoted Chicago survey in which no increase in the incidence of jaundice could be found in G6PD-deficient term black infants. And yet, two of us had encountered several instances of severe neonatal jaundice from this cause. Seeing is believing. When a survey conflicts with personal experience, maybe something is wrong with the survey. Perhaps the fallacy lies in totting up a hundred G6PD-deficient infants who are not jaundiced instead of studying ten who are.

A baffling question then arose over the typical manifestations of acute and subacute haemolysis. Did the known absence of haemoglobinuria prove that the haemolytic process had proceeded at a slow and steady rate over many days? How acute must haemolysis be to elevate the bilirubin level to 57mg/100ml and lower the haemoglobin to 8gm/100ml, and if it happened in three days, would haemoglobinuria ensue? The defence contended that, even in the severest forms of Rh incompatibility, haemoglobinuria was unknown. Fast and furious, scribbled notes traversed the benches between the medical experts and the by now bewildered counsel who, as sole permitted spokesmen in the tussle, did their best to put the niceties of intravascular physiology to an increasingly bemused judge.

A sad moment came when the specialist in developmental paediatrics bleakly listed the boy's multiple handicaps and the hopeless future that awaited him when his parents will no longer be there to care for him. Large tears coursed down his mother's cheeks, almost as if she had been brought face to face with reality for the very first time. The judge was evidently moved, for he castigated counsel for calling this witness when a deposition would have sufficed.

Summing up, his Lordship confessed that this case had caused him great anxiety, but he was satisfied that the system in the hospital was as conscientious as it could be by the standards of 1965. Investigations of a moderately jaundiced black infant today might have been exceptional eleven years ago. If he had been convinced that the infant was already dangerously jaundiced on the day he went home, he would have felt bound to award damages of the order of £53,000. In the event, he is not convinced, and therefore the claim must fail.

American Journal of Diseases of Children, November 1977

Colostrum Deficiency

SIR – I wonder if anybody has ever seen a baby die for want of colostrum.[27] Only this week I saw five very agitated mothers who evidently thought that theirs might. One had respiratory distress and another a large cleft palate, and a third persistently vomited all his 'unique maternal gift'. The mother of the fourth had a complicated delivery and was herself unwell, while the fifth had inverted nipples and was unable to produce any colostrum or milk.

All worked themselves up into a frenzy because their babies had not had their 'cholesterol' (sic), although all five babies are making excellent progress.

I am, of course, familiar with the multifarious properties of this substance, but colostrum deficiency would appear to be a new iatrogenic disease of the maternal mind, springing from the same sources which are responsible for so much unnecessary anxiety today.

British Medical Journal, February 1979

---

27. The first milk produced by the breasts during pregnancy.

Letter from Abroad
Twelve Good Men and a Dog

London – On Nov 9th, our consultant geriatrician[28] was attacked and nearly murdered. The news spread like wildfire through the hospital, kindling consternation, outrage, and dismay. The response contained all the usual reactions except surprise. Mental sickness is, after all, common and crazy people finish up in hospitals sooner or later. Coming up against a homicidal maniac is just one more occupational hazard of being a doctor. There is little more to be said, but is it really so simple?

This hospital, unlike so many of our antiquated bastions, is a splendid new building of advanced design hardly four years old and is considered something of a showpiece in our ailing Health Service. But for the sour fermentation of industrial strife and the sorry mirage of phase 3 of the building program – namely, the paediatric block – that may never see the light of day,[29] we have a building of which we can be proud. It towers impressively over huddles of little, terraced houses and the snails' pace motorway crawl from Heathrow. The vast carpeted foyer, replete with an escalator, compares favourably with many a four-star hotel, and envious tongues have been heard to wag of the 'Fulham Palace' and the 'Charing Cross Hilton'. We have four squash courts, an Olympic-size pool, a fish pond containing an original Henry Moore, and two dozen unguarded entrances.

Hospitals are public buildings to which the public has

---

28. Dr Peter Helps.

29. In due course it *did* see the light of day, but was later vacated when the department of child health moved to the new site in Chelsea.

the right of unimpeded access. People come and go freely all day.

A man walked in through the main entrance and demanded to see a doctor – a reasonable enough request. He was directed to the Accident Department but aroused the suspicions of the head nurse who 'persuaded' him to leave, thereby unwittingly saving the life of her portly consultant. (She was the first of the two heroines in this drama.) He then strayed into the Physiotherapy Department, which was noted for decorous young women and the more adventurous medical student, but devoid of qualified doctors. Again thwarted, he wandered into the geriatric ward. The intern, not long qualified, offered her assistance, which he spurned because she looked too young. My colleague Peter, hearing the argument, came to investigate. He evidently looked every inch the archetypal doctor because the man pulled out a long butcher's knife from under his coat and struck at Peter's chest. The first blow that Peter tried to parry with his arm made a long, ugly gash from the shoulder to the elbow. The second penetrated deeply into the right side of the abdomen. The third missed, Peter by then having slumped to the floor, and was embedded firmly in a nearby wooden table. The intern, a slender young woman a little over 150cm high, with unbelievable courage leapt onto the maniac's back. She effectively restrained him from pulling the knife out of the wood for the coup de grâce and made enough noise to bring assistance. My colleague was rushed to the operating room and underwent a cholecystectomy and hemicolectomy from which he fortunately recovered after a long and complicated illness. His assailant, who was apprehended, was a paranoid schizophrenic on parole from Broadmoor, our notorious asylum for the criminally insane, where he is once again safely ensconced. He is no doubt now harbouring an even more burning grievance against doctors.

One point for discussion is how so dangerous an individual persuaded a panel of so-called experts to allow him to go free, especially as his declared aim in life was to wreak vengeance on the medical profession, come what may. Of more immediate concern is the whole question of hospital security. By American standards, our security has a distinctly low profile that is carried almost to the point of non-existence. Identity disks, passes, permits and uniformed guards are practically unheard of, and the British public ebbs and flows freely through dozens of different entrances and exits. In our hospitals, serious disturbances, organised crime, and premeditated assaults are exceedingly rare. We have drug addicts like everyone else, yet pharmacy break-ins are exceptional. Our main problem is utterly senseless, mindless vandalism for which nobody has yet found an adequate answer.

The children's wards are overcrowded with visitors from morning till night. They are unprotected, but we have had remarkably little trouble so far. I can think of only five incidents in the last twelve years. Three were escapes – or perhaps I should say escapades – with children getting out and running home in their pyjamas. Only twice have I personally called our security staff for help. One was the removal of a pair of obstreperous American deportees whose emaciated, starving baby was brought in unconscious, but that is a long story in itself. The other, incredibly, was to eject Irish squatters from the ward – we have curious laws safeguarding the rights of such riff-raff in this country. It took three security officers, two uniformed policemen, one detective, and a fireman half a day to get them out. The fireman was the father of a small boy who had just had his tonsils out and, goaded beyond endurance by all the shouting, he threatened 'to sort them out if they did not bloody well... off double quick,' which they did.

We have a security staff of twelve, led by a formidable woman, and who are responsible for three district hospitals 5km apart. Their modest muster is laughable, even if vandalism were the only problem they had to contend with. I can recall at least twenty security officers in the much smaller Boston hospital in which I worked in 1958. Even then, there were discussions on whether they should carry arms, although outwardly the city was a haven of peace and respectability in those days. More recently, in Brooklyn, there was an impressive show of guards at every turn, each a potential contender for the world heavyweight title. I never saw anything remotely antisocial, nor did I ever feel particularly threatened inside or outside the hospital, but the preventive measures were reassuring in view of the many dire warnings.

A peculiarly British institution is the formal enquiry that is conducted after any untoward occurrence so that unwanted dust can be neatly pigeonholed under a corner of the nearest carpet. Our enquiry took the form of a one-man committee and a one-page report. It was couched in the usual administrative jargon but, translated into plain English, the gist of it was that boys will be boys; lunatics, lunatics; and psychiatrists, psychiatrists forever letting lunatics loose. It made two startling recommendations for tightening security: to issue uniforms to the staff and to provide a dog for patrolling the grounds.

American Journal of Diseases of Children, April 1979

Letter from Abroad
NOBMs

As some day it may happen that a victim must be found,
I've got a little list
Of society offenders who might well be underground,
And who never would be missed!

W.S. Gilbert

London – Gilbert certainly had something when he wrote this cheery little song for Ko-Ko, Lord High Executioner of Titipu. Had he lived to see the National Health Service (NHS), posterity might have been the richer by several more immortal verses. Every now and then politicians brag unguardedly how our NHS is the envy of the world, sending hollow laughs echoing round the country and even raising a few wry smiles in countries like Sweden and Switzerland. It leaves much to be desired and its ever-increasing flaws are more than a passing embarrassment. In one of our postnatal wards, an anonymous wag has put up a poster that sums up the situation perfectly. 'I was unhappy at what I saw,' it reads, 'when a voice from above cried "Smile, things could be worse!" So I smiled and, behold, things did get worse!' The start of this year has been particularly ominous. Few of us believed the situation could get so much worse. In Birmingham, 65 patients with cancer were hurriedly sent home when strike pickets of porters and other ancillary workers refused to allow food and medical supplies into the hospital. A 50-bed block at London's St Thomas's Hospital had to close as a result of the truck drivers' dispute. A disused factory in Liverpool was turned into an emergency mass mortuary to cope with the many bodies left unburied as a result of a strike by gravediggers and crematoria staff. Elsewhere, corpses were left in wards 'blacked' by porters, and militant ambulance drivers were reported to have left a sick man in the snow. 'If it means lives lost, that is how it must be. We're fed up with being Cinderellas. This time we're going to the ball,' said one of the union leaders. In my own hospital, two union shop stewards – one of them a hospital painter who is reputed not to have held a brush in his hand for three years – intimidated the boiler man to turn off the boilers. As a result, the entire maternity wing suddenly cooled down and 50 very frightened women who had just had babies or were about to give birth were hastily evacuated to other hospitals. The culprits' righteous dismissal precipitated widespread disruption, with doctors and volunteers smuggling emergency supplies past the picket lines in their cars to keep essential services going. And in Reading, an indignant orthopaedic surgeon, forced to cancel all his operations for the day by another unofficial stoppage by hospital ancillaries, hit back by turning away from his outpatient clinic anyone who admitted to being a member of a trade union. 'I was fed up with all these people making life bloody for everyone else and wanted to make life bloody for them for a change,' he said, sending half a dozen sheepish trade unionists shuffling home without being seen. At St Mary's Hospital, another orthopaedic consultant – they seem to have all the muscle – voluntarily shifted a large backlog of laundry bags and rubbish and surprised even himself by completing the task in two hours when it normally took two porters all day.

What has gone wrong? In a sudden flash of insight, I think I have found the answer. It is not just a question of insufficient money, wrong working conditions, poor pay, bad equipment, or outdated buildings. That these exist cannot be denied, but if all workers in the Health Service from Minister to morticians – and I do not wish to imply that morticians are at the bottom of the scale any more than the Minister is necessarily at the top – were genuinely concerned with the good of patients, all other problems could be overcome. In short, what is fundamentally wrong with our NHS is that it is composed of two groups of people: those who care about patients and those who do not. We need a simple but certain test for karyotyping individuals and a Chinese style of cultural revolution to purge the Health Service of all those who could not care less about the patients.

Which brings me back to Ko-Ko and his little list. I am beginning to recognise likely candidates for the qualification of NOBM (None Of 'em Be Missed), and I am getting better at it all the time. There are politicians who are afraid to condemn the worst excesses of industrial unrest and have been known to fan the flames in order not to lose votes. We are burdened with a vast administrative superstructure, mistakenly created at enormous expense. It could vanish overnight without any outward manifestation except for an immense sigh of relief all round. I have had my eye on two particular administrators for some time because they exemplify failings characteristic of their kind. One is a slave to the philosophy that 'it cannot be done'. Nothing ever does get done if he can help it. The other, and far more dangerous, makes empty promises that he has no intention of keeping. One assumes an urgent problem is being dealt with when in fact it is being deliberately delayed. Then there is the hospital engineer whose infuriating formula for any job that needs doing is to overprice it. As long as it costs too much, it cannot be approved and he does not have to do it.

Every nail and every screw appears to cost a small fortune and it is not uncommon to see a senior physician or surgeon occasionally putting a personal hammer or screwdriver to good use. Because doctors and nurses are the most closely involved with patients, they will always be the front-line and last-ditch defenders of their patients' welfare and so the role of the consultants has become crucial. Unfortunately, even among our ranks a number of NOBMs can be found, especially those who use their patients as bricks in relentlessly paving a path for personal self-advancement. As Gilbert put it:

> Such as – What d'ye call him – Thing'em-bob, and
> likewise – Never-mind,
> And 'St – 'st – 'st and What's-his-name, and also
> You-know-who,
> The tasks of filling up the blanks, I'd rather leave to
> you.

Short of a revolution, insurrection, pogrom, or purge, what can we do to get rid of the baddies who are proliferating fast and may soon outnumber those who could make the Health Service work for all its faults? Many of us must have been shocked by the infamous murder of Georgi Markov, the Bulgarian defector who was stabbed with an umbrella in a London bus queue and died of toxaemia from a miniscule pellet of ricin. I have three umbrellas in my hall stand – England is such a rainy country – and a magnificently foliaceous castor-oil plant in my study. I am looking at it now.

American Journal of Diseases of Children, May 1979

Letter from Abroad
The Fate of the Special Care Baby Unit

London – I hope I may be forgiven if I seem to be a little cynical about the proliferating number of non-events like Nannies' Sunday, National Breast Feeding Week, and the International Year of the Child. The calendar is crammed to capacity with birthdays, anniversaries, remembrance days, feast days, fast days, and holidays of obligation of one kind or another, all clamouring for the usual cards, flowers, and platitudes. It cannot be denied that they often provide a praiseworthy charitable outlet, but they can also be used for commercial exploitation and even Breast Feeding Week had its spin-off with spates of paperbacks, conferences, television time, and an entirely new range of ladies' lingerie – in fact all the usual publicity gimmicks with the exception, surprisingly, of a few free samples. True charity seems to find expression throughout the year without the artificial confines of a few days or weeks, the designation of which probably brings little extra benefit. As far as 1979 is concerned, it will always be inscribed in my memory as the year in which my own endeavours in neonatal intensive care, patiently built up over many years, were destroyed overnight and reached their lowest ebb.

On a fateful Midsummer's Day, our proverbial English weather unleashed a torrential downpour of rain that breached the frail defence of the little flat roof of the 15-year-old temporary hut housing our special care baby unit. Here, it is necessary to underline a fundamental difference between England and America where the vagaries of the weather appear to occasion neither surprise nor consternation. With us, unfortunately, it is well known that a half-inch of snowfall is enough to paralyse the whole country, bringing chaos to roads, railways, telephones, water supplies, and a good many working activities not even remotely connected with ice or snow. It is simply a question of preparedness, like sweeping out gutters occasionally so that they are not overwhelmed by the first heavy shower of rain, causing enormous damage to electric fittings and costly equipment. Thus, our special care baby unit was hastily evacuated to a single room on our sick children's ward, an exodus worthy of Noah, complete with monitors, ventilators and faith. I, for one, believe implicitly that neonatal intensive care has enhanced the quantity and quality of its survivors.

The desperate search for a new home seemed at an end when we found a vacant space that might have been purpose-built for our needs. I imagine Brigham Young might have felt the same when he came upon the land of Salt Lake City. There were three empty nurseries with various side rooms in the very maternity hospital providing most of our referrals. The reasons for our separation from our obstetric colleagues go back into a long and convoluted history and the siting of a special care baby unit in a building in which no babies were ever born has long been a source of regret. We had evolved a transport system that was probably the first in the world and of which we were justifiably proud but often felt that if our Creator had intended obstetricians and paediatricians to work several miles apart, He would surely have furnished us with an umbilical cord longer than 35cm.

We now had the nurses, the equipment, and the space. All that remained was the money to put in piped oxygen and to make a few minor alterations. It seemed little to ask but we are currently lurching through yet another financial crisis and the prospects of any contribution from the hospital budget stood at absolute zero. Then a leading children's charity – quick to grasp the immense benefit to mothers and babies – stepped in with a magnificent offer of nearly $100,000 to cover the cost. In the flush of success, thoughts gaily turned to the not-far-off opening ceremony and which member of the Royal family might agree to officiate. Little did we guess the problems ahead.

The first hurdle concerned the junior medical staff. Our junior doctors aim to work one night in three and no rearrangement of staff rotas would have made it possible to operate a special care baby unit in another building without at least one extra house officer. After four months of wrangling, soul-searching, and sacrifice, this was eventually agreed. The next bombshell came in the form of an official missive to the effect that gifts to the National Health Service, the envy of the world, were not necessarily welcome no matter how well meant or munificent. It all depends on the 'revenue consequences', the very thought of which strikes terror into the hearts of our administrators. The inevitable result is that it is now unbelievably difficult for generous people to give their money away to hospitals. Most donations have revenue consequences. Equipment needs bench space or floor space, it may have to be plugged in or, worse still, it may have to be serviced or repaired from time to time. Buildings need staff and staff need buildings. Even a fish tank needs an occasional change of water. We have just installed a computerized axial tomography head and body scanner, thanks to the grit and determination of a few stalwarts and to private donations amounting to nearly $1 million, and then only on the condition that all running costs would be found from private sources too.

After a somewhat ungracious acceptance of the offer for the new special care baby unit, the haggle began as to who was to do the work. Our Works Department was quick to dictate how it was to be done without wishing to do any of it. Since the disastrous reorganisation of the Health Service in 1974, the Works Departments are their own masters and do not take orders from hospital administrators. A project team was appointed and the project predictably came to a grinding halt. As more and more people became involved, the scheme became increasingly unrealistic and costly. Month after month went by, inflation eroding the original value of the donation until it became impossible to contain the cost within it. The most simple and menial task was costed at three or four times the amount we would spend in our own homes, and indeed ten times the cost of doing it ourselves. Offers of free paint, glass, and electric fittings were of no avail since painters and electricians were going to get their profits on these items whether we got them free or not. Add to this the subcontractors' profits, the main contractor's profit of another 15%, an inflation allowance, and a contingency allowance, and the scheme is soon priced out of existence.

So the chess game went on. Attack and defence, fortunes swaying, pieces sacrificed, and the board slowly clears. Few pieces remain, a couple of white pawns, a bishop, and two knights against two black rooks and a superior number of black pawns. But with the end of the struggle in sight, a new threat has appeared.

The financial limitations of a welfare state must be plain to any responsible taxpayer. It all has to be paid for sooner or later and the noble concept of free health care cannot command a bottomless purse. This elementary truth is often lost on a vociferous minority that is least ready to lend its services for anything less than the going rate, let alone free. The writing has been on the wall for many years and this year's new government is committed to the electorate in bringing about a long overdue reduction in public spending. The big axe is beginning to fall and at last people are waking up to the realities of life. Our hospital has been told to spend $3 million less than last year. With inflation running at 10% to 15%, new wage awards, increased fuel costs, and expanding demands on most departments, the task would seem impossible. As yet, the axe has still to fall on the really basic cause of all our ills, overmanning. We have an entire tier of administration that could disappear overnight without any sense of loss. Wages and salaries are the largest item in the balance sheet, but the slightest whisper of redundancies is enough to blow an industrial volcano, and so the axe is busily cutting patient services instead. A hospital here, a department there, a unit elsewhere. Our administrators – ironically the very tier we could so well do without – have drawn up a shopping list of proposed closures.

Heading this list is the closure of the special care baby unit. Second is the temporary closure of my colleague's Child Development Centre. In just under two weeks, a group of worthy people will decide whether we can afford neonatal care for babies who will be born come what may. It is 15 months from the day that the rain came down and a year after we saw manna from heaven.

And so endeth the Year of the Child.

American Journal of Diseases of Children, April 1980

Letter from Abroad
Great Expectations

London – An obstetrician I have the good fortune to work with from time to time telephoned me with a curious and novel problem. A foreign lady, aged 31 years and expecting her first baby in about four weeks, had consulted him about her forthcoming confinement. Not having seen her previously, he quite properly arranged for her to have an ultrasound scan. Clinically, her condition was unremarkable, but the scan showed a large swelling on the anterior abdominal wall of the fetus, correctly interpreted as highly suggestive of an exomphalos,[30] omphalocoele,[31] or gastroschisis.[32] The scan had been performed in a highly respected department by experts using the latest equipment. The question now was – or rather, the questions now were – what further investigations should be made, should she be delivered after an induction or by an elective section two or three weeks before term, and how much should he tell the parents?

Prenatal detection of fetal abnormality is a mixed blessing, and the problems raised by such unexpected findings late in an otherwise normal pregnancy are likely to be encountered more often with the development of high-resolution ultrasound imaging. Its usefulness in detecting

---

30. A weakness of the baby's abdominal wall where the umbilical cord joins it. This weakness allows the abdominal contents, mainly the bowel and the liver, to protrude outside the abdominal cavity where they are contained in a loose sac that surrounds the umbilical cord.

31. A birth defect in which an infant's intestine or other abdominal organs are outside of the body because of a hole in the belly button (umbilicus).

32. A birth defect of the abdominal wall. The baby's intestines are found outside of the baby's body, exiting through a hole beside the belly button.

neural defects, hydrocephaly, and microcephaly is already well-established. Less clear is what to do about cystic kidneys or an enlarged liver. The discovery of an exomphalos was new to both of us.

The question of further tests was relatively easy to resolve. Both serum and amniotic fluid alpha-fetoprotein levels would probably be elevated, but even if the tests discriminated reliably between normal and abnormal babies at 36 weeks' gestation, knowing the levels did not seem to offer any immediate practical application. In days happily gone by, we used to show the fetal intestine by putting a contrast medium into the amniotic sac before doing an intrauterine transfusion for severe Rhesus haemolytic disease. The same technique would presumably demonstrate loops of bowel that have spilled out of a defect in the abdominal wall provided they are not obstructed and viable, but roentgenograms during pregnancy are not respectable anymore and paediatric surgeons often overreact to the presence of contrast material in the bits they operate on, as do anaesthetists.

The discussion about the mode of delivery was prompted by the obstetrician's fear that he might rupture the sac – or rather, that the sac might rupture spontaneously during the birth. The risk would presumably be less with a smaller baby, and less still if the delivery were by an elective caesarean section one or two weeks before term, or earlier if she went into spontaneous premature labour. The question hinged on whether such sacs ruptured during labour and, like most paediatricians, my total experience of some half-a-dozen cases was not enough to go by. In the course of more than 20 years' practice, I have often been astounded by the immense swellings that have run the gauntlet of the human female birth canal and remained intact – myelocoeles,[33] encephalocoeles,[34] omphalocoeles, and even conjoined twins. I have also seen severe gastroschisis with herniated liver and spleen and masses of unhealthy purple intestine, but in which any sac had disappeared long before the delivery. I promised to put the questions to our paediatric surgeon, but before I had the chance to do so the patient was admitted in early labour.

The good Boy Scouts' motto is to 'Be Prepared.' Caught distinctly unprepared by the unexpected onset of a few contractions, the wisest plan seemed to be to postpone labour while the hitherto leisurely process of decision-making proceeded at a more pressing pace. The question of what to say to the parents depended on whether any intervention was planned. It was agreed that honesty was the best policy and that patients are entitled to be adequately informed about their state of health. On the other hand, ignorance can be bliss and silence golden. The lady was not English, and a condition such as a gastroschisis could take a lot of explaining. It was clearly unthinkable to subject her to a caesarean section without telling her why, but there was much to be said for keeping quiet about the result of the ultrasound scan if she was to go through a normal labour.

Her contractions ceased and she fortunately went out of labour as our paediatric surgeon confirmed that omphalocoeles rarely rupture during delivery and that those which had ruptured probably did so long before labour.

---

33. A type of spina bifida in which the neural tissue of the spinal cord is exposed.

34. Protrusion of the brain and the membranes that cover it through an opening in the skull. Incidentally, when I was a medical student Dad explained to me the difference between exomphalos, omphalocoele and gastroschisis, and I remember clearly thinking at the time how lucky I was to have this knowledge 'on tap' at home.

Based on an analysis of his last 70 cases, his experience was reassuring. The discussion had the added benefit of forewarning him of a possible emergency repair now seemingly done with sterile dura specially imported from German crania, and he hastened to the operating room to make sure he had an adequate supply in stock.

The following week, the membranes ruptured and she went into labour. As happens in all good fiction on these occasions, an obstetrician, an anaesthetist, and a paediatrician converged on the labour ward at 2am. The choice of physician over surgeon at the delivery had been dictated by several elementary considerations. It is not difficult to wrap up a bit of omentum on a temporary basis, but skilful resuscitation is not everybody's forte, and who but a physician would recognise whether the baby had a chromosomal disorder or other congenital abnormalities? A selection of clear, plastic, non-adherent sterile dressings had already been purloined from the operating room, there was a 'silver swaddler' on the resuscitation trolley, and I had a roll of unsterile but microbially irreproachable 'cling-film' sandwich-wrap in my car.

One of the pleasures of having to attend a delivery at 2am in recent years is the tranquil atmosphere promoted by a good obstetrician and a good anaesthetist. Gone are the days of maternal distress, cries of anguish, and the shouting of people exhorting some poor woman to push or not push as the case may be. Epidural analgesia must surely be one of the greatest blessings bestowed on women of child-bearing age by modern medicine, and the curious fanaticism for 'natural childbirth' by some is quite incomprehensible to me. Its one occasional drawback as far as I am concerned is that it has encouraged the presence of fathers at deliveries. A few agonising screams would soon drive them to the most distant part of the building, but now that mothers are wreathed in smiles under the blissful relief of an effective epidural, they jollificate in their sport coats, cameras in one hand and often a drink in the other, as if it were some kind of birthday party, which of course it is. I admit I am prejudiced, but the trouble with being a paediatrician is that we see the abnormalities – the sudden catastrophes for which most fathers seem to be totally unprepared.

This particular father was exceptional in that he looked anxious, apprehensive, subdued, and thoroughly ill at ease – more so when he realised that a paediatrician had been called in. He went and sat miserably by himself in a corner, but cheered up a little when I told him that I was merely there to make sure I should have no work to do. Normal babies cannot be had to order and abnormalities sometimes happen, but I said that it was an inexplicable fact that my services were usually superfluous when I was present and urgently needed when I was not. He seemed reassured by this unscientific explanation and said nothing more until it was all over, when he shook my hand effusively and could not thank me enough, as if it had all been my doing.

The baby, incidentally, a 2,912-gram (6½ lb) girl, was perfectly normal – an eventuality that we had not considered. If there is a moral, and I am not saying there is, it is surely: It is better to do nothing than to do something when nothing should be done.

American Journal of Diseases of Children, September 1980

Case Conferences – Why?
A Paediatrician Questions

If you have been to one, you will know what I am talking about. If not, you have missed nothing. I refer, of course, to the 'case conferences' organised by social workers in suspected child abuse. I must make it clear at once that I have nothing against holding conferences in general, in fact the very reverse. In medical practice, conferring, consulting and communicating are essential. So is good record-keeping. The one worthwhile by-product of these child abuse conferences is the typed summary which is then circulated to all those who may be dealing with the problem. But typed reports can be circulated without having to hold conferences and there are better ways of conferring and consulting. That most general practitioners share this view is borne out by the fact that few ever bother to attend. In an analysis of such conferences in this area two years ago, there were no GP attendances at all in Ealing, Hammersmith and Fulham. And yet, the general practitioner's contribution is unquestionably one of the most important.

The trouble with case conferences is that they are an appalling waste of time. Social workers have come to accept them with a certain relish. Bearing in mind the kind of people they deal with, it is infinitely better to sit round a table talking *about* them than actually talking *to* them. With about 300 conferences per year in the area, each lasting an average of just under an hour, this could be a full-time 40-hour-a-week job for a month for some. The time would be well spent if it could be shown that case conferences served an unequivocally useful purpose. As it is, they have been promoted on a nationwide scale without any evidence that they are worth the time, effort and money invested in them. A few telephone calls, letters and visits would achieve as much if not more in a fraction of the total professional time, and is by far a better way of arriving at the facts.

Like the flowers that bloom in the spring (tra la!), half of the members who attend have nothing to do with the case. At best, there is always a good deal of hearsay and fictitious gossip. Hard facts, like the medical histories from the GP's personal records, are often missing. There is a tendency to call conferences in indecent haste before the facts are known in the vain hope of finding them from people who know next to nothing about the family. The inevitable result is to call a second conference when a few facts have been collected and to go on calling conferences until the necessary information is complete. Conferences beget conferences and still more conferences, like a biblical pedigree.

The question is not as innocent as it may appear. In cases of undoubted non-accidental injury, it is right and proper for senior and junior social workers to meet repeatedly to decide and carry out an agreed plan of action – a difficult and thankless task which doctors are only too glad to abdicate after providing the necessary medical evidence. But in the majority of cases, the medical evidence is lacking. Many injuries are genuinely accidental, self-inflicted, acquired in the course of reasonable chastisement or just 'idiopathic', like so many other conditions known to medical science. The case conference may then become a status platform for a pressure group determined to involve itself in the affairs of patients contrary to the attending doctors' wishes, and in the process doing more harm than good. Conference members tend to see themselves as a decision-making body, condemning families to 'At Risk' registers and unwelcome visits from social workers. Not surprisingly, this sometimes causes great anxiety and distress and needless extra work for the family doctor. Why, then, convene a case conference before attempting to find out the medical evidence on which it would have to be based? It is an interesting question which I hope somebody else will try to answer.

Faculty News, 1980

Letter from Abroad
Send for the Engineer!

London – My Chief 30 years ago[35] (I shall have more to say about him this year when he celebrates his 85th birthday) endeared himself to us in many ways, one being the way he might suddenly bellow in the middle of a ward round, 'Send for the Engineer!' An urgent summons could be dispatched by all kinds of minor defects, for instance a flickering X-ray viewing box or a squeaking crib. The cribs all had overhead telescoping lights which you were supposed to push up out of reach of small fingers, but they rarely worked so 'when they were up they were up, and when they were down they were down, and when they were only halfway up they were neither up nor down'. Elbow-taps were another special *bête noire* because they invariably drew nearer and nearer the wall until they defied the most determined and pointed elbows. Up would go the familiar cry, scattering starched aprons in the direction of the telephone, and within seconds a flushed, perspiring workman would appear, stoically bearing his twin burdens of a heavy canvas tool-bag and social injustice.

The extraordinary thing about those far-off days is that a man always came instantly and, under the baleful glare of our Chief, fixed what needed fixing on the spot. *O tempora mutantur, et nos mutamur in illis.* It now takes ten weeks to change a light bulb and two 'engineers' to do it. A few months ago, they held this large new hospital to ransom and all but succeeded in reducing it to an empty shell. It is a tragi-comedy worth telling because, like the famous shot at Concord, Mass., which echoed around the world, the blow

---

35. Dr Bernard Schlesinger.

for freedom and salvation struck at Charing Cross Hospital on that fateful day in December has meaning for us all.

How it began is obscure, but for over two years the engineers had worked a money-spinning shift system which had fewer men on day duty, when there was work to be done, than on evening or weekend duty when there was little. Rumour had it that some of the men were earning more than the professors. A new supervisor lost no time in clearing up the mess and before long, management and men were on a collision course. The clash came at the end of September. Two men, both union representatives, were told to change the filters in the operating rooms. This they refused. To be precise, they did not refuse to change the filters, but they refused to carry them, arguing this was 'labourer's work'. Management had visions of needing four men to change a light bulb: two porters in blue overalls, one to carry the lamp and the other the ladder, and two engineers to effect the change. All 18 ORs ground to a halt, the two ringleaders were sacked, and some 40 engineers walked out in sympathy. A familiar enough tale so far.

At first, the unofficial strike went unnoticed. The professionals and supervisors went on working and the ORs were soon back to normal. Thanks to the shift fiddle, it seemed to make little difference whether the men were working or not. Clearly, they had to do something more if their action were to succeed. The dispute was strictly unofficial and other workers were wary of joining in until they could see which way the wind was blowing. So the engineers put up a little wooden hut by the goods entrance, installed a couple of chairs and facilities for brewing tea, and set about blocking the delivery of essential supplies. As time went on, they added a few more home comforts: a transistor radio for the latest racing results and, more importantly, a charcoal brazier from which the distinctive aroma of sizzling pork sausages would occasionally come wafting. Management countered by asking suppliers to send non-union drivers and, when that failed, getting essential supplies through in private vehicles. However, the ruse that gave most rejoicing was the simple expedient of diverting incoming goods to the front entrance. For over two weeks, the strikers kept guard and brewed their tea in wind, sleet, and rain at the back, while everything was coming in normally through the front. Moreover, management had taken the sensible precaution of ordering a substantial surplus while the going was good.

What nobody had bargained for was our precarious dependence on oil. The hospital tanks held only two weeks' reserve at the most and the tankers had to come through the goods entrance. Oil is power; power is oil. The deployment of non-union drivers soon led to an ugly situation developing at the main Esso depot, with the distinct possibility of a nationwide stoppage unless they were withdrawn. It was not that the drivers had anything against the hospital or were particularly sympathetic towards the engineers – in fact, the very reverse – but union rules forbade them to cross any picket line, official or not. But the use of non-union labour was more heinous than original sin itself.

Then began the desperate struggle for survival. All cold surgery was cancelled, the accident and emergency department was closed, patients were sent home. One by one, the wards were shut. Lights were dimmed, the heating was turned at first down and then off. The few remaining patients huddled round electric fires as the oil in the tank dwindled lower and lower. Every day, full tankers arrived at the gate, only to be turned round by the pickets within spitting distance of the oil-starved, cavernous storage tanks. The level of fuel had fallen so low that sludge from the bottom was beginning to foul the machinery.

The death throes of the hospital became national news as the media focussed increasingly on the drama enacted at the back gate. The Prime Minister denounced the heartlessness of the strikers in no uncertain terms. Public opinion was roused and, within the hospital, feelings began to run high.

The children's department reluctantly closed its doors, to conserve the last few drops of fuel. Three precarious premature babies in the special care unit, two of them on ventilators, were evacuated to the adult intensive care ward, adding to the already frantic anxiety of the parents. Distressed and upset, they went out to remonstrate with the strikers, a crowd gathered and an angry scene developed. That night, the 15-year-old brother of one of the babies described on a radio 'phone-in programme the heartlessness of individuals who place the lives of tiny babies in jeopardy to serve their own ends. He went on to tell two million startled Londoners that conditions at the hospital were so bad that the nurses had not had a bath for weeks.

On a cold November day, another ugly scene unfolded before shocked viewers when the cancer patients on radiotherapy were sent home. The head of the department, one of the kindest and most respected members of the staff, went out to the picket line to plead with the strike leaders. Before nationwide television and press coverage, they hurled unprintable abuse on his white hair. 'They are not good men,' he told reporters sadly, as he came away. It was the worst he has ever been known to say of anybody.

By now, the stage was set for the final showdown. The end was as sudden as it was unexpected. The junior doctors were holding a heated argument about the crisis when an attractive young house officer in her first post berated her male colleagues for their pusillanimity. They were all a lot of chicken-livered spineless sheep, she declared with anatomical inaccuracy but telling effect, and marched bravely off in the direction of the picket-line to do battle single-handed, to prove that she meant it. By the time she got there, she was at the forefront of a formidable army of doctors, nurses, technicians, students, patients, and members of the public, united in purpose and militant in mood. Astonished reporters and television cameramen watched with unconcealed glee as nurses, armed with buckets of water, doused the pickets' charcoal brazier to extinction, and a hefty rugby scrum flattened the wood-shed with one charge. The building, having been erected without planning permission, was illegal anyway. The strikers, heavily outnumbered by a crowd which clearly meant business, took to their heels and fled 50 yards up the road where they huddled miserably on a traffic island. At that very moment, a tanker turned the corner. The surprised driver, fully expecting to have to go back with his load, was met with open arms, open gates, a resounding cheer and a hero's welcome. As the first thousand gallons poured into the empty tanks, the news was flashed and splashed from Land's End to John o'Groats. *ANGELA'S VICTORY*, *ANGIE'S ARMY TRIUMPHS*, and *ANGEL TO THE RESCUE*, proclaimed the headlines. Hearts were lifted, steps lightened, bated breaths unbated, and many a moist eye fired by the girl's inspiring example and photogenic appearance. Messages of congratulations poured in from all over the land. It was like V-Day all over again.

Tanker followed tanker. Within days, the tanks were filled to overflowing. As long as the rank and file of Angela's Army controlled the gate, the tankers came rolling through.

It had not been appreciated until then that union workers abide by a curious code of ethics. This forbids brothers (or sisters) from crossing a picket line. Who or what is immaterial. If the pickets tell you to keep out, you keep out and if they tell you to come in, you come in. By definition, a picket is somebody immediately outside a gate. If a dozen chimpanzees lined up outside a gate, they would presumably qualify, but you can't have a picket 50 yards up the road on a traffic island. Angie's Army showed that ousting hostile pickets and substituting friendly ones can bring last-minute salvation and lasting peace.

Oil is the lifeblood of the civilised world. Great nations will be held hostage by those who manipulate its power. Let Angie's Army be an inspiration.

American Journal of Diseases of Children, March 1981

The Fourth World

The First World is the ancient and civilised world. It is the bit we live in. It is us. The Second World is – or was – the New World, in other words, North America. The Third World is the deprived world. We are not allowed to use the adjectives 'uncivilised', 'undeveloped', or even 'developing' anymore. No country likes to be thought of as backward or barbarian, whereas a term which implies that somebody else is to blame is eminently acceptable.

I did not appreciate the existence of a Fourth World until last week when I listened to a thought-provoking talk by a visitor from Exeter to our Obstetric Unit. He, in turn, had learned of it from the French community health service, France being a country well known for its imaginative, energetic and successful onslaught on maternity and child welfare and perinatal mortality.

In every country and in every city, however well off, there is always a small minority with the worst record for employment, education, nutrition, health and life expectancy. These are the people who live in slums or worse, who never learn to read or write because they do not go to schools, who have large families because they do not know any better, who are perpetually on the verge of nutritional deficiency and who lose a high proportion of their babies. No comparison of perinatal mortality between countries or cities is valid unless this minority is numerically identified. It is high in London but low in Stockholm. The much lower perinatal mortality in Sweden is not so much due to better medical care as to a totally different population.

None of this is especially new or surprising but the problem has not been all that clearly spelled out before, nor possible solutions suggested. Every doctor knows about Social Classes I to V. The Fourth World is Social Class VI. It is that group within our midst who choose not to take advantage of the medical and social services available to them. All suffer from this self-imposed neglect but especially the children who, even before birth, are neglected in utero. The mothers do not attend ante-natal clinics and when they do, they do not come regularly. The fetal loss is high either way, the birth weights are lower, there are more complications, more abnormalities and more deaths.

The incentives for better care introduced in France in the last decade simply do not work for the people of the Fourth World. It is almost as if the financial inducements for attending health clinics have no meaning because money itself has none. Poverty is a way of life, so deeply ingrained that it is probably unalterable. Certainly, paying these people to go to the doctor has not worked in France, and is unlikely to do so here.

What then is the answer? More psychiatrists? More social workers? Experience with Social Class V would suggest that these are even less likely to succeed here. But the general practitioner stands a good chance of acceptance and can deliver health care to where it is needed. Already, one or two pioneering GP frontier-posts have been formed. One is in the Midlands in a desperately poor slum area. The primary health team has set itself up in the very heart of a Fourth World community, bringing a New World dimension to hovels we hardly care to think about.

If there is a Fifth World, it is the place where the GPs who dedicate their lives to the welfare of Fourth World communities go. Religious people call it Heaven.

Faculty News, July 1981

A Pukka Sahib

B.D.R. Wilson retired a few months ago. He was associated with St Thomas's Hospital for nearly fifty years – a remarkable innings by any standard. As every student knows, the history of St Thomas's Hospital goes back 800 years, so Brian Wilson's half-century spans a sixteenth of that long and illustrious history. The way he has shrugged off the passing of time is also remarkable. I first met him briefly twenty-five years ago when he looked like a youthful Colonel Blimp who might have seen service in India. All these years, he has not changed one bit and it would not surprise me if that is just how he looked on his first day as a preclinical student as he strode purposefully through the portals of the medical school. That was a lucky day for the Children's Department which was to boast of a higher output of consultant paediatricians than all the other London schools put together, mostly during the time when Brian was its heart and head. Just what made the Wilson vintage so special is hard to say, but special it was. His remarkable flair for picking the right chaps had something to do with it, for he picked me and at least one Foreign Secretary. But most of all, he captained a truly happy team most of whom were thereby persuaded to make paediatrics their chosen career.

On the evening of November 7, as a full moon was rising, a large number of not-so-old boys and girls gathered to wish him well in his retirement. What has the moon got to do with it, you may well ask. Nothing at all, of course, except that it happens to be historic fact and happily coincided with some inspired shafts of Instant Sunshine, yet another of Brian's notable alumni. I hope they make a record of their number so that we can all buy it and hear it again and again. As a piece of musically potted biography it is much better than anything I can put into prose. I shall not compete with those merry verses, but here are a few personal vignettes from the years after 1957 when Brian Wilson took over as head of the department, a surely merciful day for all.

It was something of a family gathering because Brian is basically a family man and managed to infuse the essence of a family into the running of the department. It was as if he had one family at home and another at the hospital. To know the one was to know the other. An important event for the department was Christmas. We always went to the Christmas show together and laughed uproariously in perfect harmony of minds, although rarely of music, because Brian had usually premedicated us well and we always had a splendid firm dinner after. On the other hand, the event of the year for the Wilsons of Woking was Guy Fawkes' Night. Brian, as a true ultramarine-blue conservative, has always regarded the attempted destruction of Parliament as a matter for personal vengeance. For months before the fateful night, he would painstakingly build a mountain of carbonaceous combustibles at the bottom of his garden. Anything that might burn furiously would go on the growing heap. This would eventually be topped by an effigy which looked a bit like Brian because it wore the Wilson wardrobe. Then, on the top of all this, Brian would pour several gallons of paraffin and petrol so that the slightest spark set off a holocaust which terrified neighbours in all directions. Meanwhile, his three small boys had assiduously accumulated a vast hoard of high explosives from months of pocket money and other legitimate earnings. Each had his own firing position and supervisor. The general idea was that they should take it in turn to let off a firework one at a time, but in practice any semblance of rotation was rapidly lost in a fusillade of indiscriminate pyromania. 1961 was a particularly disastrous year. A stray spark accidentally dropped into one of the boys' ammunition boxes, more or less setting the entire lot off in one go. Rockets, Roman candles and bangers cascaded wildly in all directions, another spark set off the bonfire prematurely with a bang which shook the house to its foundations and soon the whole garden was a raging inferno, with Brian running manfully between overwrought elderly relatives in need of resuscitation, a small boy in need of comfort and compensation, and several fine rose beds in need of rescue. Monsieur Hulot could not have done better.

How the animals suffered! When he is not trout fishing, Brian is something of a naturalist and his extended family include an unusual fauna of dogs, cats, bantams, a parrot, a fox cub, an assortment of insects and a python. He rescued a rusty old drip-stand from somewhere in the bowels of the hospital and humped it manfully to Waterloo where he had to run the gauntlet of the ticket inspector's gibes. The drip-stand, done-up, made a splendid perch for the parrot, a beady-eyed beast with a beak which would cut like a knife through a bone as thick as a human metacarpal. One day, the parrot escaped and flew to the top of a neighbour's tree. He scorned all entreaties to come down and the siege lasted all night and into the next day. At last he condescended to avail himself of a few tempting morsels whereupon Mrs W, with great presence of mind and having nothing better at hand, and doubly mindful of her metacarpals, took off her dress and hurled it over the bird. Having trapped the infuriated parrot, the problem was how to get out of a stranger's garden in a state of undress. Until the problem was solved, the safest course appeared to seek refuge behind the nearest bush, lending a new meaning to the old saying that two birds in a bush are worth one up a tree.

The python lived in a clapped-out old incubator. Exactly how Brian man-handled this to Waterloo Station and what comments he had to endure this time we can only guess, but it was unkindly rumoured at the hospital that his senior registrar was plotting to give him a coronary. Little did anybody know at the time that those measured strides between Waterloo, Westminster and Lambeth and a good many more incongruously down the Mile End Road, were being accomplished in the face of increasing leg pain. The next few years were to test his great stoicism to the full. Denis Cottom, his colleague, was fatally crushed by a rampant French lorry. This was a tremendous blow to the hospital, to British paediatrics and to Brian personally. The work of the department went on somehow but more bereavements followed, and then came the greatest sorrow of all.[36] It takes a special kind of courage to turn round a large cortege of stunned students and limpingly lead them to the nearest pub to drown a mutual sorrow.

Many months later, and almost too late, Brian was willing to let the surgical chaps have a go at the pipe-work. The old ship was back on course and sailing strongly, and he could afford to consider himself at last. 'I wonder if the graft will hold,' he mused, referring to some six inches of Wilsonian aorta, while dishing out liberal measures of sherry from a hastily improvised bed-bar to a steady stream of visitors. Before long, we were regaled with the same furled umbrella and purposeful steps from Waterloo to Lambeth, with the difference that this time they were probably pain-free. As if to prove the point, I once caught him laughing uproariously at a bedraggled-looking bunch

---

36. Wilson's middle son died tragically at the age of nineteen.

of pickets outside a building site where work had ground to a halt. 'Those chaps think they're on strike,' he said, wiping his eyes, 'when in fact they've all just been sacked.' He did not have a particular grudge against the working classes provided they were working. That is why he never could resist those spy-holes and spectator platforms at building sites. All those chaps toiling by the sweat of their brows was enough to make a fellow's chest swell with pride. But as for lazy layabouts, especially the prolifically reproductive, it was as if the blighters' unemployment benefit came solely from his own taxes. To break up a strike is to strike a blow for the British Empire and therefore irresistible to Brian. When the railwaymen called a one-day stoppage, he was determined to carry on as usual, although it was obvious the rest of the country would simply have a bonus bank holiday. We camped out in Clapham and drove in extra early to beat the anticipated traffic which never materialised. When we got to the hospital, it was deserted. There is no point taking the kids to hospital when you have unexpectedly got the day off. It was a pyrrhic victory even if there was no work to do. As a regular commuter dependent on the railway service, he got to work despite the railwaymen, and that was good for a laugh in itself.

Brian has a fruity voice with a delightful gruff chortle, promoted to an engaging guffaw when trade unionists, Labour politicians, foreigners and the gainfully unemployed are discomfited. For students to see him at his best meant shuffling round Mary Ward one morning a week on what was called 'The Breast Round'. After his homily on the way of sows, cows, goats and horses which would have done justice to Farmer Giles, it was remarkable that any mothers remained to go on with it or why the nurses did not hand in their resignations instantly. But with the children, the same forthright approach paid off. All little boys were 'George' which must be a very uncommon name these days because in seven years we only had two real ones. Not having had girls of his own regretfully, his rapport with little girls was less instant. Some of them were 'Popsy', those with curly hair and ribbons were 'Fairy', and I am afraid not a few of them were 'George'. They had no special name for him, neither did we and, as far as I know, nor did the students. We should have done because he was a Pukka Sahib.

St Thomas's Hospital Gazette, Summer 1981

Letter from Abroad
Fringe Pediatrics

London – There is a subtle difference between originality and novelty, as between fame and notoriety. Fringe medicine is the waste product of true invention, thriving on news and glitter in a soil of human frailty. Medical humbug has been around for a very long time and will no doubt go on flourishing as long as there is a demand. Its invasion into pediatrics is relatively new and has been spurred on by the public's increasing preoccupation with the minds and bodies of babies, including those not yet born. Whether or not this is a good thing is open to argument. When is ignorance truly blissful? For better or for worse, people have developed an unquenchable thirst for the technicalities of anything from childbearing to childrearing, and the more technical the better. Ironically, our respective infant food industries are under attack, although they have probably done more than most to spread good health education. In sharp contrast are the growing number of unconventional practices that we patiently have to put up with as long as they are reasonably harmless. Fringe pediatrics is not necessarily the frill of a fine service. The danger is that it may become the whole carpet.

Take, for instance, the case of the woman who adopts a baby and wants to breast-feed.[37] It does not have to be a woman. I seem to remember last year reading about a New York gentleman who, aided and abetted by his

---

37. Note the hyphen in breast-feed. My father's later use of this word adopted the modern 'breastfeed'. Likewise, words such as 'house-physician'. I have tried where possible to stay true to the original printed material.

endocrinologist, decided to do likewise. Why not, one might ask. It cannot hurt the infant provided he gets enough milk from a bottle. The pediatrician's role is to make sure the baby gets enough food. The rest is not pediatrics and, in the case of the hopefully lactating Manhattan male, it is not even gynecology. Yet, I have just read a serious article by a woman pediatrician who adopted a baby and attempted to breast-feed. It cost a small fortune in lactational aids and stimulators, all to little purpose if one looked at it bluntly as a farmer would. Infant feeding has always attracted fringe practitioners and no pediatrician can fail to be aware of an entirely new repertoire of strange manoeuvres in that direction. For most of its long and checkered history, the object was to save women the tedium of feeding their own babies. Now, having won their victory, they have suddenly become a captive market for all kinds of curious contrivances for making the homely variety. One wonders how people coped a hundred years ago. Electric pumps are in great vogue. Although we use them regularly on our postnatal wards, I fail to see the sense in renting them for use at home for several months at enormous expense. Although I am naturally glad to see a well-fed, thriving baby, I must confess that I was not impressed when a woman medical student recently brought her baby into my lectures to be breast-fed. Another lady was politely removed from a fashionable restaurant when she started giving the baby his home-made dinner.[38] A small paperback I had the misfortune to review expressed the view that mothers should breast-feed for sexual gratification if nothing else. As a consumer, I still firmly believe that the nutritional needs of the diner should take priority over the emotional needs of the chef. The syndrome of the baby who is not doing well, and the mother

---

38. How times have changed!

who had read all the wrong books and knows everything better, is easy to spot. The babies' records show that they have never been adequately examined because they are always feeding, while on the mothers' bedside tables are piles of books on mother-craft and numerous cans of beer. Somehow the idea has got around that drinking, especially beer, makes the milk flow, as if the breasts could ever behave like a pair of kidneys. If there is one crusade which I am sometimes tempted to begin, it is to stop mothers drinking titanic draughts of fluid and giving themselves equally titanic diureses on the unphysiological premise that it will make more milk.

Childbirth is a particularly popular target for cult groups and has become befringed as if nobody has ever been born before. We have had fathers coming in for some time, so much so that if he is out playing golf people jump to the conclusion that there must be something wrong with him. More recently, fathers have been coming in to watch caesarean sections, where the chances of complications are much higher. The ultimate in sharing the experience is to bring the other children in, as is done in at least two London hospitals, although fortunately not my own as yet. Mothers arrive with strong views – and if they do not have them, their boyfriends (who are not necessarily the fathers) do – on whether to deliver standing up, sitting down, or lying in a variety of positions. Much commercial ingenuity has gone into designing delivery-room furniture to cater for these needs. In the Soviet Union, there is a vogue for performing the delivery under water. We have yet to go to that extreme, but already we have to cater for those who want the baby born in the dark and to the strains of personal choices of music. All, of course, are subjected to the unavoidable cacophony of squelches, borborygmi, road traffic, and jets on their way to and from London Airport. There are more trappings apart from special music: skin-to-skin contact before the cord is tied, immersion in a bath of water, body massage, and, the finest delicacy of all, eating up the placenta at the end. But why should not mothers eat their placentae, if that is what they want to do? There are, in fact, several valid practical objections. It is far too large for any one mother to eat alone, so what does one do with the leftovers? The catering staff naturally refuse to give up any freezer space and the mortuary does not seem the right place if it is going to be used for a later meal. Another problem is, who is to cook it? The mother is hardly in the position to do so herself, and the nurses, who are not exactly noted for their culinary skills, usually balk at an order for a slice, fried or grilled, medium rare. The ward domestics are not so fastidious, but their attribute has been known to put ordinary people off a coffee break. Anyway, placentophagy (the name with which this practice has been graced) is bad for histopathology.

Womb music has had a good run, but has mercifully been quiet recently. It began as a test for fetal hearing but rapidly degenerated into the familiar exaggerated claims that it made their brain grow, produced superior intelligence if not musical geniuses, etc., etc. We had already been through all that with mothers taking whiffs of oxygen and ozone, followed by a fashion in decompression suits that were, at least, good for a laugh. We then went through a phase of tape-recorded heartbeats and ordinary thumps from a big brass drum to fool babies into thinking they were still in utero. James Thurber wrote, 'You can fool too many people too much of the time, but you can't fool the kids.'

The latest fad is to nurse preterm babies on sheepskins. Those who believe in the real thing are strangely intolerant of the man-made-fibre substitutes, while not a few of my colleagues have swallowed the extravagant claims hook, line, and sinker. The unashamedly unconverted, like me, wonder why several years of evolution have not endowed mothers with woolly chests, at least for the duration of the puerperium. Is it perhaps because in prehistoric times the babies of hairy-chested mothers died out after inhaling the hairs or getting fatal hairballs? It had to happen sooner or later. Two London babies ate their artificial sheepskins and gave their neonatologists a nasty fright.

American Journal of Diseases of Children, September 1981

Letter from Abroad
Grüsschrift

London – I hinted before that I wanted to write something about my first chief on his 85th birthday. Thirty years have gone by since I was a very green intern on his service. He retired 20 years ago, and we have not met for a long time, nor has it been my privilege to know him well. However, those early 1950s were a time in my career that I still cherish and remember clearly.

Bernard Schlesinger has always had friends all over the world, and a whole generation of paediatricians will be thinking of him and wishing him well in his typical English village retreat in the lush Berkshire countryside. Generous, magnanimous, and a natural leader, he inspired affection, admiration, and respect. Contemporaries will remember his work on the relationship between streptococcal infection and rheumatic fever long before antibiotics and at a time when the cause was still a theory. Rheumatic fever and Still's disease were his lasting interests, and his observations on the latter in the *Archives of Disease in Childhood* are among the classics of the paediatric literature. Typically, he was one of the first in the field in the use of steroids. Compliant and generous friends in the United States sent him adrenocorticotropic hormone (ACTH) long before anybody else had any or even knew what the letters stood for. His observations provide the basis of much of our current treatment. For example, by a curious quirk it was discovered years later that nephrotic children treated by other paediatricians with cortisone or prednisone did not grow as well as those treated by Bernard with ACTH. He was fascinated by oddities, especially if nobody else had ever seen anything like it before. In 1950, it was hypophosphatasia, and he was not content until he had collected all three cases in Europe. He then unearthed a strange new form of hypercalcaemia. This was followed by a phase of the Cornelia de Lange syndrome, or typus degenerativus Amstelodamensis as he called it, and, for a while, we had an impressive collection of these in the ward. But, someone so eminently practical could never confine himself exclusively to the esoteric, and one of his most far-reaching achievements was to found the first premature baby unit in a London teaching hospital, now one of the most prestigious in the land.

The National Health Service had just been launched. Everybody was frantically busy, and visiting consultants were frantically busy. In those days, consultants had sessions in many different places, time was always at a premium, and there was never a moment to lose. A typical half-day session began with a brisk gallop around a full ward, followed by a crowded outpatient clinic, a lecture or two, a pile of letters, and a frantic dash to the other side of town for a repeat performance. The system only worked if we juniors were fully mustered and ready in the front hall the second that he arrived. This, incidentally, is something we did cheerfully, in sharp contrast with the present. Work began on the street side of the front door and ended in a grand finale of instructions on the street side of his car door, which we slammed obligingly for him before he roared off to his next assignment. He had just bought himself a new Jaguar with an innovatively low profile and, for months, had a plaster on the top of his smooth head where he repeatedly banged himself in the course of these hasty exits and entrances.

Despite his superb carrying voice, it was not easy to keep within earshot. He heartily despised the one and only lift that creaked and groaned painfully up and down the centre of the Victorian building. How University College Hospital (UCH), London, survived all those years on one antiquated elevator defies imagination. We have 30 elevators at the new Charing Cross Hospital, London, and could do with six more. Admittedly, we also have 15 floors, but even this would not have deterred Bernard who bounded up the stairs, two at a time, hotly pursued by the intern and the two residents in varying stages of respiratory distress. As a dedicated squash player in the peak of condition – he was still playing and winning well into his 70s – he always outpaced us easily and would arrive on the paediatric floor talking to us lesser mortals who were still on the floor below. His ever-hopeful question, 'Do you play squash?' to all newcomers became something of a legend. Whenever possible, we tried to signal a frantic 'no' because he was a very good player, and the chances of getting soundly beaten were overwhelming. One luckless new junior fell right into the trap. 'I'll see you at six tomorrow,' said Bernard, who added kindly, as an afterthought, 'Better have your breakfast first,' in case the junior imagined he was expected on court in the evening instead of the morning. In the event, it was the usual one-sided match.

That junior was Benson, whom Bernard called Bunson because he was an inveterate spoonerist. Bunton, the surgeon, was Bunter. Palfrey, my successor, was Poultry, and I was let off comparatively lightly as Hubert. He roared these inversions down the phone or the length of the ward with unconcealed gusto. You had to think fast because if he asked to speak to Allnut, he could mean Nutall in orthopaedics, Nutting at the War Office (which he contacted frequently as consultant paediatrician to the Army; 'Get me the War Office!' became another nostalgic catchphrase), or the chief pharmacist who really was called Allnut. Then there was Trumpet. Actually, there was no Trumpet either at UCH or at Great Ormond Street, but there was a Trumper in one of the laboratories, a Tromper in the dental department, and a Trump in administration.

The names of foreign visitors were mangled without mercy, but, as hardly any of them spoke English, it probably did not matter. Conversation could prove an uphill struggle but Bernard, soldier that he was, would battle on bravely. 'This child has gastroenteritis,' he might declare very slowly and several decibels above his already generous sound level. 'Do you have gastroenteritis in Bulgaria?' After much explicit and imaginative sign language, we would be rewarded with the vigorous nods and happy smiles of comprehension. 'The next child has coeliac disease. Do you also have coeliac disease?' More signs and more nods.

Those were days when every child had his or her latest offering in a glass-covered pot under the cot. Bernard patiently worked his way around the whole ward, by the end of which we had established that pneumonia, nephritis, cradle cap, and squint occurred in Bulgaria, whereas hypophosphatasia and typus degenerativus Amstelodamensis did not. Undaunted at having exhausted that line of enquiry but spotting a bluebottle aimlessly buzzing around the room, he might suddenly ask the startled visitor, 'Do you have bluebottles in Bulgaria?' Another favourite ploy at this stage would be to remember all of a sudden that he had promised to take his mother out to lunch. On this implausible pretext, he could make a hasty getaway, leaving the rest of us to suffer several more hours with travellers from Ahmadabad to Zanzibar.

In casting doubt on these lunch appointments, we did him a grave injustice as we were soon to find out. Late one evening, we admitted a little girl with severe croup. Bernard was in town that night, so we asked him to come in and have a look at her. He arrived soon after midnight, attired in the full regalia of a gala night at the opera, and scattering terrified nurses in all directions. I cannot swear to a top hat, but I vividly remember a long black cloak. Striding into the ward like a cross between Count Dracula and a latter-day von Eisenstein from *Die Fledermaus*, he took one look at the child and summoned the rectal tray. Spellbound, we watched him peel on a glove, still in his cloak. We had, of course, examined the child carefully from top to toe and examined every orifice bar one. In a case of croup, it did not seem particularly relevant. Holding his gloved index finger aloft briefly like a starting pistol, he suddenly rammed it down the astonished child's throat, retrieved it smartly before she had a chance to bite it off, and declared with much satisfaction that she did not have a retropharyngeal abscess. He then scribbled an indecipherable prescription in Latin, which must have been handed down from the great George Frederick Still himself, containing splendid ingredients like tincture of cardamomum, spiritus camphorae, and aqua bromoformis. The extraordinary thing about Bernard's concoctions is that they always worked. He said she would be better by the next morning and she was.

Impulsively generous as always, he insisted on taking us all to the same opera the following week, Menotti's *The Consul* – dress informal, thank heaven. This was the first occasion on which I was privileged to meet his family, notably his son John, later to become the renowned film director, and that dignified elderly lady whose existence we had so shamefully doubted. She at once endeared herself to us when she had occasion to reprove Bernard, who was his usual ebullient self, by saying, 'Bernard, be your age!' neatly bridging three generations in three words. She was asking the impossible, of course. He had boundless enthusiasm and energy, which secured his place among the leaders of the profession to the day that he retired. Even today, it would be fully in his character if he gave local causes the same zest and inspiration that he brought to paediatrics in his long and distinguished career. Regrettably, we do not have *Festschriften* in England, let alone *Grüsschriften*. I hope I have started something.

American Journal of Diseases of Children, February 1982

Life Without Charity

We are lucky enough to live in a society which accords individuals the right to hold their own views, however much we may deplore them. The trouble is that people with strong convictions are rarely content to keep these to themselves. You will always find vociferous minorities imposing unpalatable beliefs on the silent and suffering millions.

LIFE is a new organisation of reputedly some fifteen thousand members. Life, of course, is what medicine and surgery are all about. Therefore, one could be justified in thinking that a society dedicated to life might have a larger and active following from doctors. The very opposite is the case because it is essentially an anti-doctor group, directed at obstetricians and paediatricians in particular. The attack on paediatricians is the more surprising since this specialty has a rather outstanding record when it comes to saving lives. Only sixty years ago, one in ten children born died in the first year. Today's infant mortality is a little over one in a hundred. Our perinatal mortality is a fraction of what it was and one need look no further than the nearest neonatal intensive care unit to see why. If LIFE exterminated all paediatricians overnight, the neonatal mortality would be catastrophic.

LIFE has two fundamental aims. One is to stop therapeutic abortions. The other to force aggressive surgery on grossly malformed babies with lethal abnormalities. Most paediatricians believe in making these unfortunate infants comfortable and allowing nature to take its course. But letting these babies die, argues LIFE, is murder as surely 'as cutting their throats with a knife'. It has deluged the Director of Public Prosecutions with numerous deaths from severe hydrocephalus, meningomyelocoele and other major defects, conditions common enough to be seen once or twice yearly in all paediatric units. All have necessitated a shameful abuse of police and professional time at the expense of the long-suffering taxpayer. It has plagued doctors and administrators with frivolous demands and has invited paramedical staff to inform on doctors and nurses who allow babies to die peacefully when aggressive treatment might have prolonged their misery by a few weeks or months. It is only a matter of time before we may see such babies taken into custodial care by officious social workers for the sole purpose of frustrating responsible medical treatment. Bizarre as it may seem, children may be removed from the care of reputable physicians and reputable hospitals not only against the wishes of the parents but also their medical advisers.

LIFE does not claim to do anything for the millions of children who die needlessly in other parts of the world. It does nothing for the handicapped, the halt, the lame, the blind or the deprived – except to increase their number. It gives nothing to save lives in hard-pressed neonatal intensive care units. Its members do nothing to provide practical help to those in need. Despite a lot of glib talk about fostering and adoption of severely mentally and physically handicapped infants, we have yet to see any recognisable contribution towards their welfare. To spread pain, suffering, hardship and misery is life without charity.

Faculty News, April 1982

Favourite Remedies

We all have our favourite remedies and it would be fascinating to make a collection sometime. My own peculiar paediatric repertoire includes alcohol, corks, silver charms and Parkinson's Old-Fashioned Humbugs.

Alcohol

Giving babies alcohol is sure to raise a few eyebrows, but the idea is not as outrageous as it may seem. Most fetuses get a taste during pregnancy and a good many might not have been conceived without its assistance. Breast-fed babies go on getting a few drops here and there, and it is also present in a few highly respected remedies such as Eumydrin, not to mention that universal panacea for every infantile ill wind, our old friend the Gripe Mixture. Presumably there is nothing sinful in babies having a little alcohol when the occasion demands it because a Mohel will regularly give a baby a swig before circumcision. Alcohol has the distinct advantage over other treatments in that it is usually to be found at home, it does not need a written prescription and it does not cost the Health Service anything.

Teething hardly ever causes any symptoms but mothers are determined that it should. I tell them to rub in a little sherry or brandy, which is not only cheaper but a lot more effective than other teething remedies. Perhaps, having got the bottle out, most parents have some too, so everybody is happy.

I sometimes use brandy in the special care baby unit on babies with recurrent apnoea. There are various ways of dealing with this alarming (*literally*, because these babies are always closely monitored) complication, but none simpler than putting a drop of brandy on the tongue every two or three hours. It gives the babies a renewed zest for life, the parents are intrigued, the nurses quite like it because there is usually plenty left over, and only the registrars disapprove since they would much sooner use the far more toxic theophylline. In fact, alcohol has a high calorific value – 7 calories per gram, compared with sugar which has only 4 calories per gram. I may therefore use alcohol to boost an otherwise severely calorie-restricted diet in cases of malabsorption when every single calorie counts. Vodka is best here as it is almost pure ethyl alcohol and virtually tasteless. I get the bemused parents to buy half a bottle and, as in the advertisement, 'they never knew how babies are made until they found the Smirnoff'.

Cork

The use of a cork to hold a needle while making the other end red-hot for enlarging the hole in the latex teat of a baby's feeding bottle is already well known. A less familiar indication is in the treatment of nosebleeds. This common emergency always looks worse than it is and some of the manoeuvres employed by well-meaning relatives may exacerbate the problem by raising the blood pressure or dislodging the clot. The act of swallowing also dislodges the clot, hence the cork. It is impossible to swallow with one's mouth open. Therefore, the child is made to lie on the side of the bleed with a cork between the teeth and a tissue to spit or dribble into. Everybody keeps calm, a clot forms in a few minutes and the crisis is over.

Silver

Unlike my other three favourite remedies, the silver charms are not intended to be taken by mouth in case they are accidentally swallowed and thereby necessitate additional investment in the form of a pot and a metal detector.

I use silver charms for nail-biting. But the principle has wider applications for children of different ages and sex and for other afflictions such as obesity and enuresis. The parents are asked to buy the girl a charm for each perfect nail. Five perfect nails earn a total of five charms, ten perfect nails ten charms. Each new charm is bought by the girl herself with some ceremony at a jeweller's of her own choice. Ten perfect nails for one month earns her a bracelet and, for three months, getting all the charms permanently soldered in place. Relapse in the first three months results in a return of the collection to the parents' pawn. By the time the girl's nail-biting is cured, her parents must expect an outlay of about £50 at current prices, but it is a worthwhile investment and it is not as if it's going into the bottomless hole in the Health Service.

Humbug

Lastly, Parkinson's Old-Fashioned Humbugs. For the benefit of those not familiar with this confection, these generously proportioned boiled sweets have an interesting shape, are striped like zebras and are dispensed in the sort of tin which most small boys like to keep.

I reserve humbugs – and the name is a happy coincidence – for hysterical disorders. The treatment is always well received and is, in my experience, far more effective than a year's regular attendance at a psychiatric clinic. It has the great virtue that it gives the child a chance without appearing to admit that it was all put on. It is essential to explain that this particular humbug contains a secret ingredient in the stripes which is not found in any other sweet. One humbug must be taken religiously every four hours by day for a full five days' course and all symptoms will disappear after the second dose. I once had a boy who crowed like a cockerel. After months of psychiatric treatment, he crowed like three cockerels. After two humbugs, he was cured!

I reserve the humbug treatment strictly for hysterical symptoms with a high nuisance rating, but often use other sweets for coughs, colds, sore throats and some ear-aches. Lollipops and Spangles are a lot cheaper than linctuses, each 'dose' stays longer in the mouth and the children swear by the treatment.

Faculty News, July 1982

Ethical Decisions

Mrs Collins phones up her District Hospital and asks for the maternity department. Her general practitioner has just told her that she is thirteen weeks' pregnant and she wants to make an appointment for the antenatal clinic. She explains that she is 36 years old, this is her first baby and she is anxious to have an amniocentesis as she is afraid of having a Down's syndrome baby on account of her age. She is offered an appointment three weeks later and the booking clerk reassures her that it is quite unnecessary for her to be seen any sooner. In due course she arrives at the sixteenth week, only to be told that she is a month out in her dates and is in fact twenty weeks pregnant. To her dismay, the doctor tells her that she cannot have an amniocentesis. For one thing, it is not the hospital's policy to perform the test in women under the age of 37, and in any case it would be too late to do anything about an abnormal result even if she had one. She is eventually induced at 42 weeks and delivered of a 2.8kg girl, who not only looks two weeks early but also has the unmistakeable features of Down's syndrome. The parents are greatly distressed and refuse to see her. The hospital social worker is informed but meanwhile the baby develops the symptoms and signs of heart failure, and is moved to the special care unit. The paediatrician is reluctant to treat her, even medically, the nurses are divided, the social worker insists she is transferred to the Regional Cardiac Centre and the parents want nothing done at all. What would you do?

The story has a familiar ring and is not far removed from the truth. It raises complex issues of relationships between doctors and patients and between different members of staff; the meaning of consent and the rights (or wrongs) of refusing treatment; abortion and the difference between euthanasia and allowing to die; and, indeed, the wider questions of the sanctity of human life on the one hand and its quality on the other. To ask, 'What would you do?' presupposes that such a decision is made from responsibility and based on a knowledge of ethical reasoning. It can, of course, also be thrown open to public debate, from consultants to students, or the senior nursing officer to the ward domestic. The difference is that, in real life, ethical decisions are left to relatively few people with the necessary knowledge and defined responsibility, whereas general discussions aim to teach and sometimes provide a helpful prelude to making the best choice. The distinction is important because almost anyone confronted with an ethical question would at once volunteer a 'gut' response. But ethical judgements are not based on purely emotional reactions any more than a surgeon might stop doing open-heart surgery because some of the nurses hate the sight of blood. Nor can they be based on empirical rules such as refusing to perform abortions under any circumstances whatever. The law provides a framework but not all ethical problems have legal overtones and there are many practices which may be legal but would be unethical just as the reverse is also true, as for example on the question of confidentiality between doctor and patient. Moral issues also intrude, but there are many religious persuasions in the world and what is moral in some may be sinful in others. They produce easy solutions without any attempt to recognise or understand the full implications. Therefore, the nurse who says: 'I do not know. I should first like to hear what more experienced people have to say' is on the right path for forming ethical judgements.

If the ethical approach is not emotional instinct, or

sticking to a book of rules, or abiding by the law of one's faith, what is it? Here are four definitions, only one of which is right. To choose the correct one implies a grasp of what it is all about:

- Ethics is the study of right and wrong.
- Ethics is the study of the underlying reasons for deciding to do what is best in the face of conflicting choices.
- Ethics is a set of guidelines which should lead to the right solution.
- Ethics is the study of how different people react to difficult alternatives.

Although it is the longest, the second definition sums up the subject best. It stresses the importance of reasoning and the existence of at least two, if not more, possible alternatives. Finally, it avoids the black-and-white concept of what is right and what is wrong altogether by using the word 'best' for a particular choice in a particular situation in which the rest may be less good but not necessarily bad.

The element of choice is fundamental, for when there is no choice there is no ethical problem. For example, a premature baby of 1.5kg should be nursed in an incubator in a Special Baby Unit if the facilities exist and there is really no safe alternative. Equally, a normal 3kg baby should not be parted from the mother and again there is really no acceptable alternative. In between are varying degrees of risk to the baby and it is when the advantages begin to match the disadvantages that an ethical decision has to be made. I have chosen this example deliberately because this particular decision is now often dictated by emotional reasons without a careful weighing up of the possible risks to the baby. Babies of 1.5kg or even less may be taken out of their incubators to be fondled by parents or siblings, or put to the breast, although they get nothing this way and must still be tube-fed.

A careful consideration of the various alternatives is like chess. It is necessary to go over all the possible moves and their consequences. A good player will never underrate his opponent or make a risky move in the hope that his opponent will make a mistake. Among the wide choice of possible moves, some will be good and some bad but the best is that which is the most likely to succeed. This can only be done by according each option some kind of arbitrary value, so that they may then be placed in rank order. Thus, if the baby in question is nursed carefully and with the least possible disturbance, the chances of a successful outcome cannot be far short of a hundred per cent whereas any benefit to the baby from taking him or her unnecessarily out of the incubator are probably zero. By adding up the relative values of all the arguments for and against, the preferred choice will emerge.

Who Will Benefit?

Before looking at the infinitely more serious problem of Mrs Collins and her baby, it is necessary to clarify one further principle, namely for whose benefit ethical judgements are made. Is it for the patient or the parents, and if so, which parent? What if the interests of the mother and the father conflict? Or is it for society as a whole? Few would be happy if such decisions are made mainly for the benefit of the doctor. But what if they are made solely to appease the Director of Social Services – a common occurrence these days – or worse still, at the behest of a small, fanatical pressure group? Once again, relative values must be given to all. For the low birth weight baby in the incubator, this is easy. A high mark must be accorded for the good of the baby, an intermediate mark for each parent, relatively low marks for the needs of the doctors and nurses and probably no marks at all for the Director of Social Services or any pressure groups. Different people might well give different marks but it is highly probable that relatively speaking the values will be similar and the final answer the same. In other words, it is necessary that most other people who apply the same principles arrive at the same conclusions in all but detail – known in ethical terms as 'universalisability'.

Mrs Collins should have been seen sooner, as no doubt her general practitioner intended. He might have interceded on her behalf, but we do not know if he was asked. Perhaps the booking clerk took on rather more than she should have done but the practice is common. The doctor in the antenatal clinic does not come out well. She – and no offence is intended in choosing a woman obstetrician here – was clearly in error technically by misdiagnosing the stage of the pregnancy and failing to confirm this with a scan. One is an error of commission, the other of omission. Neither harmed the baby and, if made without negligence, could be considered pardonable. Unfortunately, as it happened, the stage of the pregnancy was crucial to the question of whether to perform an amniocentesis, overriding a matter for ethical decision-making by a technical irregularity.

Legally, Mrs Collins could have had a termination of pregnancy for a Down's syndrome fetus and, as she had already indicated that this is what both parents would have wished, we may assume that religious considerations did not apply. A crucial question is how far it is justifiable to offer the chance of making an antenatal diagnosis to women over 37 while denying it to women of 36 and under. The stated risks of having a Down's syndrome baby are 1 in 800 in women aged between 30 and 34 years, and 1 in 300 between 35 and 39 years. The risk at 36 can only be marginally lower than at 37, so why the insistence on the latter? Certainly, by the age of 30 or less, the risks of aborting a normal fetus heavily outweigh the chances of detecting an abnormal fetus, although many would argue that this is mitigated by the prospect of further pregnancies. However, what it really amounts to is how far the laboratory can cope with the workload. Restricting the test to 40 and over involves our laboratories in some 20,000 tests for a likely 400 Down's syndrome babies – a mere third of the total born in England. At 35 and over, our laboratories would have to process five times as many for only double the number of Down's syndrome infants. But, whatever value one might accord the expedience of the laboratory service, it would still heavily favour the right of this particular mother to the test.

It has already been argued in Court that no woman has a legal right to an abortion, although of course she may with justification claim damages for wrongful advice and for the burdens of having to bring up a handicapped child. Had she proceeded with an abortion, this could have been an ethical decision. However, the parents' instant rejection of the child after birth was almost certainly an emotional reaction, no doubt rationalised by the antenatal errors. It would be too much to expect parents to make a reasoned ethical decision immediately after the birth although they may be helped to do so subsequently. Until then, who is *in loco parentis*? The paediatrician? The midwife? The social worker? Society? Some self-appointed guardian of public morality?

The Right 'Not to Treat'

I hope I have said enough to show that whoever takes on the task has the knowledge and experience to evaluate in turn all the alternatives, to assess all the pros and cons of treatment and non-treatment and, at the same time, distinguish between the various degrees of action and inaction. The management of heart failure in an infant can escalate from simple rest to tube-feeding, fluid restrictions, sedation, oxygen, cooling, diuretics, bleeding, assisted ventilation, further investigation and open-heart surgery. Each of these has a rateable value for success or failure, and for safety or danger. When the baby also has Down's syndrome, many of these measures could be construed as forms of euthanasia by those unfamiliar with the same treatment and its results in babies with uncomplicated congenital heart disease. It is necessary to rate the likely short- and long-term future, and it is not permissible to ignore the feelings of the parents and the members of the medical and nursing team. It is not always appreciated that physicians and surgeons have the right to withhold treatment if they choose that as the best course. Thus, a Director of Social Services who decides that a child should have a treatment which he himself does not possess the skill to provide and which the physicians and surgeons at a centre of excellence are not prepared to undertake, may then take it upon himself to place the child in willing but less prudent hands to suffer a more tortured death.

The final computation is often a long and laborious exercise, and may still be inconclusive in which case the weight given to each argument is checked once more as carefully as the recount in a close finish of a parliamentary election. The American Code of Ethics for Nurses states:

'The nurse's primary commitment is to her patient's

care and safety. She must be alert to take appropriate action regarding any instances of incompetent, unethical or illegal practice by any member of the health care team, or any action on the part of others that is prejudicial to the patient's best interests.'

As a guideline, this is admirable, although it says nothing about the quality of life, like turning off a ventilator when the patient has sustained irreparable brainstem death. Ethics recognises the existence of 'persons' and 'non-persons'. An old man of 90 in a deep coma after his third stroke is a non-person, in the sense that he has been permanently deprived of all human faculties except breathing and a heartbeat. In the context of abortion, a malformed fetus is a non-person. The precise definition of a non-person has still to be resolved but the concept has been with us for a very long time.

The following code of allegiance is still used at Florence Nightingale's own hospital:

'If you see anything which you believe to be prejudicial to the well-being of your patients, it is your duty to report it forthwith to your immediate superior *and then meddle no further therein.*'

Midwife, Health Visitor & Community Nurse, November 1982

Letter from Abroad
Of Morals and Mercy

London – The prosecution – or should I say persecution – last year of one of our colleagues in a criminal court on a charge of murder is now a milestone in medical history. In the absence of a Falkland crisis to overshadow the event, the case commanded much public interest and exhaustive media coverage, leaving little unwritten or unspoken by the time the dust had settled. The jury's acquittal after only two hours' deliberation was hailed as a triumph of good sense and rectitude. The trial and its aftermath will go on rumbling for a long time. Life and death will also go on, but, for infants, neither can ever be the same again.

The main details are probably well known to readers. An infant with Down's syndrome was born at the Derby City Hospital, and the senior paediatrician was called in to confirm the diagnosis and to talk to the distraught parents. Derby, the home of Rolls-Royce cars and fine porcelain, is a small town in our industrial Midlands with a population of 250,000, about the size of Rochester, NY, although there any resemblance ends. It has more than its fair share of poor people and is surrounded by an exceptionally lush countryside that is famous for its potholes. These geographical asides are not particularly relevant, except that a paediatrician of such a community must steer thousands of children safely into adult life and is sure to earn a special place in the affection of countless local people. It is also important not to forget that, despite the 5,000 miles between Derby and Rochester, NY, the indictment of a paediatrician for murder is an extraordinary event of profound significance for paediatricians everywhere.

The parents hoped that the infant might not live. It is a fact that he was somewhat unconventionally sedated with dihydrocodeine tartrate and that he died in just less than three days. Within a matter of hours, an undisclosed nursing auxiliary informed an organisation called LIFE that, in turn, at once telephoned the Derby Criminal Investigation Department, alleging that the infant had been starved to death and demanding an urgent police investigation. LIFE is an anti-abortion group that claims to have 15,000 members. They are not interested in the millions of deprived children in the world who die of starvation and neglect, nor in the halt, the lame, the blind, or the suffering, except perhaps to swell their numbers. They give nothing to children's charities or neonatal intensive care units. Despite glib talk about adoption and fostering severely subnormal children, I have yet to see any significant contribution for their welfare.

Having lost the battle on the issue of abortion, which is now lawful, LIFE – and I have little doubt they have their counterpart in the United States – have turned their frustration and wrath on paediatricians who allow infants with gross and lethal malformations at birth to die peacefully. Paediatricians, who have a remarkable record for saving lives (the infant mortality is a tenth of what it was at the beginning of the century), have come increasingly under attack. For the most part, this has been directed against the conservative treatment of severe spina bifida. Using a network of secret informers, they have made numerous unsuccessful complaints to the Director of Public Prosecutions, including one about me. The infant with Down's syndrome in Derby afforded the organisation its first taste of *Schadenfreude*.

It is, of course, true that an otherwise normal infant with Down's syndrome is very different from one who has a lethal malformation. However, it seems hardly credible that an infant might die of starvation in less than three days. The question remained whether he died from the cumulative effect of a drug. This was resolved dramatically in the middle of the trial when the paediatric pathologist called by the defence produced convincing evidence of fibroelastosis of the heart, intracranial calcification, and a congenital lung pathologic condition, all of which had escaped the Home Office expert who was not a paediatric pathologist. This resulted in the charge of murder being withdrawn and one of attempted murder being substituted, a clear admission that the infant died of natural causes. From then on, the outcome could hardly be in doubt, but if the defence had not been so skilful, the result might have been otherwise.

A remarkable aspect of the case was the overwhelming support from the general public, and the profession, for the accused. Three fellow paediatricians appeared on his behalf as did the president of our Royal College of Physicians. All testified that there were times when the prolongation of life was no longer in the interests of the patient. Summing up, the judge advised the jury 'to think long and hard before concluding that doctors of the eminence we have heard have evolved standards that amount to committing a crime'.

A much-debated aspect of the case has been the propriety of ordering 'nursing care only'. A classic example is the infant with Down's syndrome who has duodenal atresia.[39] This, too, has been in the news recently. The first case was especially unfortunate as the mother had apparently had an amniocentesis in early pregnancy, and the result had been wrongly reported as normal. When signs of intestinal obstruction developed in the infant, the parents decided against surgery and that she should be allowed to die. The

---

39. Absence from birth of part of the duodenum.

hospital's social worker – and how she came to be involved is not clear – took a different view. Social workers stopped being faithful members of the medical team a long time ago, when they were made wholly responsible to an external Director of Social Services, covering a wide geographical area and with wide powers. The Director directed that the infant should have an operation. The child was accordingly moved to another hospital where the surgeons – and all were unanimous on this point – refused to operate without parental consent. By this time, she was receiving her fifth day of intravenous alimentation and time was running out, so the case went to court. The learned judge thought the parents had every right to refuse surgery under these circumstances, whereupon the Social Services had the infant taken into Care, thereby effectively making them the legal guardians. They then lodged an appeal in the appeal court in which three judges had no option but to overrule the previous ruling and direct that the operation could go ahead without the consent of the parents. A willing surgeon was found at yet another hospital, and the operation was successfully completed around the 12th day. All this took place more than a year ago, and to my knowledge, the infant has been in a foster home ever since. Amen.

This case, like the last, highlights the difficulty of applying a legal solution to a problem created by medical advances that have outstripped the law. I have encountered the dilemma of a Down's syndrome infant with duodenal atresia thrice. One was operated on before we could be certain of the diagnosis; chronic heart failure developed, and he died after 15 miserable months of torture for him and his parents. I counselled strongly against surgery in the second case, much to the mother's and grandparents' relief, but the father, who was a physician, wanted an operation;

while we were still arguing the pros and cons, the infant died of natural causes. I am sure the father suspected otherwise, although his suspicions were quite unfounded. I am equally sure that, finally, he too was thankful.

The third case was particularly illuminating. I again advised against surgery. The parents were deeply religious and were obviously torn. They consulted their priest, who urged them to do everything humanly possible to save the infant's life and to pray for divine strength. They then asked the bishop for a second and superior opinion. The bishop thought long and hard and then, before committing himself, asked for the operative mortality. A week had gone by, and it was only right to point out that this was now considerable. 'It is for God to take life, not a surgeon,' said the great man.

American Journal of Diseases of Children, December 1982

Comment by Michael Barrie

This story refers to the case of Dr Leonard Arthur who in 1981 was tried for the attempted murder of John Pearson, a newborn child with Down's syndrome. John Pearson was born on 28th June 1980 – as well as Down's syndrome he had additional abnormalities of his lungs, heart and brain. Shortly after the birth, Arthur talked to John's parents and then wrote in the case notes, 'Parents do not wish the baby to survive. Nursing care only.' He prescribed dihydrocodeine to be given 'as required' in doses of 5mg at four-hourly intervals. The child died three days later.

Arthur was a kind, gentle, and compassionate man who cared deeply for his patients and their families. A great supporter of the weak or poor, he was motivated by firm Christian beliefs. The response of his medical colleagues in Derby was immediate and unanimous, and resulted in his continuing to work while awaiting the three weeks' murder trial. Arthur was defended by George Carman who in his closing remarks said, 'He could, like Pontius Pilate, have washed his hands of the matter. He did not, because good doctors do not turn away. Are we to condemn him as a criminal because he helped two people [the mother and child] at the time of their greatest need? Are we to condemn a doctor because he cared?'

Arthur was acquitted of all charges. The community, and especially the many parents of children for whom he had cared, lent their vociferous support in the long months preceding the trial. Inevitably the ordeal took a terrible toll on Arthur, shattering his self-confidence, but he bore no grudge against those who had accused him. He died aged fifty-seven, on Christmas Day, just two years later.

It was an important test case: the trial brought to public attention the dilemmas for doctors in treating severely disabled newborn infants. Arthur felt strongly that doctors should always act in the best interests of the child, with the full support of the parents. In some cases this meant not prolonging the child's life, in order to prevent future suffering. Opinion polls taken at the time of the trial indicated huge public support for Arthur's approach. The outcome of the trial confirmed that 'nursing care only' is an acceptable form of treatment, and that administering a drug to relieve suffering is not an offence, even if it accelerates death. Ambiguities remain, however, and if a doctor (or anyone else) intentionally kills a child, however disadvantaged, this would still be considered to be murder.

Whooping Cough Controversy

We all have patients who become worked up and worried over nothing and I do not doubt that general practitioners get more than their fair share. There is enough anxiety about without deliberately creating more, which is exactly what all the scaremongering about whooping cough has achieved. Every time the Department of Health launches another campaign on pertussis vaccine – and I usually hear about it from the patients or the media, rather than from official channels – my heart sinks because I know I am in for another deluge of letters and telephone calls from frightened parents. Many have already been to their family doctors, so what I have to say is a repeat performance, but in the hidden depths of every discerning parent lurks the glimmer of a true scientist with an unshakeable faith in the value of duplicate observations. It is not a question of a bishop's blessing being any better than the parish priest's, but a united Amen has the same kindred potency that trimethoprim confers on sulphamethoxazole, not to mention the pre-medicating influence of people who tell parents they should worry even if you say they should not.

My calls usually come from three kinds of parents – those whose babies are too young to vaccinate, those from whom pertussis vaccine has quite correctly been withheld on medical advice, and those with children of school age who were not given pertussis vaccine as infants and in whom three jabs of the single vaccine now are of questionable benefit. All have been led to believe that their children are in imminent danger of death or brain damage from the ravages of an epidemic which is sweeping the country and which only the vaccination of babies and toddlers can halt. The awesome words '*Whooping cough is a killer!*' are on everybody's lips. It would be more true to say, 'Whooping cough was a killer.' The mortality started to dwindle with the discovery of antibiotics and has been negligible for twenty years. There have been five deaths in England and Wales so far this year, with six in 1980 and two in 1972. There are more cot deaths in one year than from whooping cough in thirty years. The really unforgivable aspect of the current publicity is the way parents have been bludgeoned with the risk of death, which is now virtually non-existent. The same can be said for brain damage, which must be excessively rare, for in my 30 years' experience I have never knowingly seen a handicapped child whose condition could reasonably be attributed to whooping cough, although I have attended several cases of vaccine damage.

Whooping cough is no longer the lethal or crippling disease it once was and it is wrong to frighten the public into thinking that the clock could ever be turned back.

I accept that it is responsible for an unpleasant and often prolonged cough. I also accept that the drop in notifications in the 1970s may have been partly due to the vaccine which, in recent years, has been reasonably safe. I do not accept that pertussis vaccine given in infancy protects children when they go to school. I do not accept that children are the only victims, or that it can only be had once. I see fewer than half a dozen cases a year and have seen none since June. I have no evidence that the epidemic, apparently raging elsewhere, has affected West London. And, I am unhappy about a campaign aimed directly at the public instead of the profession.

We have been regaled with stories of the sacrificial vaccinations of some very important babies, whose sheltered care makes a chance encounter with a *Bordetella pertussis*[40] exceedingly remote until school age, by which time any protection will have long worn off. This is when the good general practitioner comes into his own, because whooping cough is an eminently treatable bacterial infection. It is susceptible to erythromycin, ampicillin and trimethoprim/ sulphamethoxazole which should be used readily and early in suspects and contacts, adults and children alike, and especially when there is a new baby in the home. Antibiotics cannot cure the cough which is due to the endotoxin of dead bacteria, but they lessen the severity and the duration of the illness and limit the spread.

Good general practitioners do not need advice on the symptomatic relief of mild whooping cough, or to be told that bad attacks with cyanosis should always be treated in a place where there is oxygen. It is still not sufficiently well known that severe spasms in the early stages respond quickly to a short course of oral prednisolone, 5mg three or four times daily, for one week and tailed off in the second. The spasms disappear in three or four days. There is absolutely no reason why any child need suffer a prolonged, let alone fatal, illness in this day and age. It would be interesting to know the circumstances of those who did.

Faculty News, January 1983

---

40. The causative agent of whooping cough.

Letter from Abroad
Campaign of Terror

London – Good news is no news, only bad news, as journalists will tell you. The mini-epidemic in the middle of 1982 could not have come at a more opportune moment. Thus, in the comparative lull of the usual tales of murder and destruction, the predicted rise in whooping cough notifications was almost welcome news. Epidemics have occurred regularly every four years since notification of the disease became statutory, and 1982 was an epidemic year. In fact, annual notifications in England and Wales have been comfortably under 20,000 in the last ten years, except in epidemic years, when the numbers have generally trebled. Deaths had long dwindled to less than a hundred by the middle of the 1950s and, in recent years, have not exceeded a dozen at the most. Pertussis vaccination was introduced nationally around 1958, and notifications undoubtedly declined thereafter, but nobody has ever explained why the mortality came tumbling down years earlier, or why the quadrennial quivers continued. There is a distinct impression that the disease has become milder, to which must be added a certain scepticism about the effectiveness of the British vaccine and not a few reservations about its safety. The net result was a fall in its acceptance to 30% by 1978.

This, then, was the scene in the middle of 1982 when the notifications began to climb. Our Department of Health, prompted by its vaccine-oriented medical advisory committee, suddenly erupted into uncharacteristic hyperactivity. A stream of statements, bulletins, and memoranda poured forth through television, radio, post and press. Hardly a day passed without the latest whooping cough returns appearing somewhere. 'Pertussis Peaks Again', 'Epidemic Claims Another Victim', or 'Killer Disease Strikes Again' (all the way from the first to the 12th) were typical headlines. A recorded message phone-in service encouraging parents to have their children vaccinated was set up. Terrified parents were greeted with a hair-raising series of paroxysms from a child close to expiry followed by a diatribe on the imminent dangers of death, brain damage, and lasting lung disease. The message ended, in the tradition of such commercials, with the urgently voiced hysteria-toned exhortation: 'If your child has not been vaccinated, do not delay. There is an epidemic. Get your child vaccinated now!' More coughing. The campaign of terror was on.

The recommended age for administering pertussis vaccine was raised to 2, then 3, and finally 6 years. As usual, paediatricians were the last to hear about it. Panic-stricken parents of 5-year-old children were telephoning me to be told one thing, only to be told something different by the media from a leapfrogging Health Department. Polite enquiry whether primary pertussis vaccination of older children was soundly based on field trials, and scientifically respectable, extracted the convoluted reply that there were no such trials, but that there was no reason to think that it would not be equally beneficial. Much publicity was given to the vaccinations, like sacrificial lambs, of the Health Minister's own infant daughter and, with even less justification, bonny Prince William. Of all the infants in the land, the latter's supremely sheltered care would render a chance encounter with a *Bordetella pertussis* about as remote as catching green monkey disease.

At the height of the scaremongering, I was getting two

or three letters or telephone calls a day, mostly from parents whose infants were too young to vaccinate, in whom pertussis vaccination had been medically contraindicated, and from parents whose children were of school age. The awesome words 'Whooping cough is a killer' were on everybody's lips. All believed their children to be in imminent danger of death or brain damage. All thought that whooping cough was an infectious disease that only young children caught, and vaccination would confer protection for life. It had not occurred to them that, like flu, it could be had repeatedly, that adults had it too, and that immunity rarely exceeded two or three years. In fact, there was little evidence of an epidemic in London, and admissions for whooping cough to my wards remained something of a rarity. I can honestly say I have never knowingly seen brain damage caused by this disease – in contrast with a few cases of vaccine damage – and have encountered only two deaths, both preventable, in 25 years. Pertussis today is an eminently treatable condition. A course of erythromycin or sulfamethoxazole-trimethoprim will curb the growth and spread of the organism and, when necessary, a short course of steroids will stop severe coughing spells. Harrowing tales of prolonged hospitalisation and demise make me wonder what kind of treatment might have been used, or not used. Most of my patients, even infants aged only a few weeks, are home inside two weeks, and few are admitted anyway. Why all the fuss about a dozen possibly mismanaged whooping cough deaths, when we have an annual toll of 1,500 cot deaths, 2,000 child deaths from accidents, and 2,500 avoidable perinatal deaths?

It is an interesting question, and it is difficult to believe that political factors do not enter into it. Most of the arguments center around vaccination. Once the medical advisory committee had committed the Department of Health to nationwide vaccination, it could not readily go back, despite the embarrassingly high attack rates in children given the British vaccine in the Medical Research Council trials in the 1950s, and the disturbing reports of encephalopathy, sometimes followed by severe and permanent handicap. The current vaccine is probably safer and more effective than those used earlier. Promoting it costs next to nothing since the Child Health Centres, their physicians, and health visitors already exist, unlike the massive investment needed for research into cot deaths, accident prevention, and neonatal intensive care. In the eyes of the Health Department, what hath no need of gold glitters. The currently quoted risk of a severe reaction is one in 100,000 for eligible infants who have had all three doses of triple antigen. Just what it is for an older child completing a course of pertussis vaccine on its own is not known, but will no doubt tax the ingenuity of the statistically inclined in their multitudinous mathematical manipulations of convulsions and comas that could have occurred for other reasons. Nevertheless, children remain inconsiderately two to five times more likely to have an acute neurologic illness after whooping cough vaccination than at any other time. A Vaccine Damage Payments Act became law in 1979; since then, approximately 600 youngsters have received substantial compensation for severe handicap after pertussis vaccination – an average of 25 a year since vaccination began. What this means in real terms is anybody's guess, but the sullied reputation of the first British vaccines will take a long time to fade.

Meanwhile, we gaze West where pertussis-antigen vaccines are given routinely with apparent safety and without argument, and we gaze East where in some places pertussis vaccination has been abandoned, and notifications are no higher than anywhere else. It is all very well for us professional Januses, but is it right to drag the public into the fray?

American Journal of Diseases of Children, September 1983

Media-Induced Maladies

The media and medicines have much in common. Used carefully and caringly, they confer great benefit. They also both have their side-effects and overdoses occur. The bliss of a little ignorance is better than too much health education or education of the wrong kind. A healthy interest in medical matters can all too easily merge into morbid curiosity. High-street bookshops are stacked with medical information, expressly packaged for public consumption, and it is only right that it should be varied, topical and continually updated; but if saturation point has not already been reached, it cannot be far off.

Most of the information put out by the press, in books and on radio and television, is the work of professionals and is responsible and restrained. Like all industries the media has its entrepreneurs, extremists, evangelists and cranks. The public is always eager to buy but is not always in a position to distinguish between good and bad. Moreover, even the best health educators have to accept the influence of market forces. The proprietor of a newspaper may be forgiven for being more interested in the circulation of his paper than the factual content of one or two medical articles. Television producers are perhaps more concerned with entertainment than with whether they are upsetting a few patients or their doctors. Not surprisingly, a few people get hurt and media-induced maladies are as apparent today as food poisoning.

The most common manifestations are worry and anxiety. It could almost be said that these are the luxuries of a media-addicted Western society. The many poor millions of the world, with more than enough legitimate cause for worry and anxiety, cannot afford such luxuries. Media-induced anxieties are rarely more than a passing nuisance to the doctor called upon for reassurance.

A more serious situation develops when patients on, say, an effective and widely prescribed anticonvulsant are confronted with a disturbing sensation-seeking report in a newspaper to the effect that this drug is poisonous or deadly; they may stop taking it before getting proper advice. This type of report should always be thoroughly filtered first through responsible medical channels.

The converse is also true whereby patients, often with incurable diseases, read about a revolutionary new treatment in Russia or America and flock off in search of it at enormous expense, regardless of their doctors' advice. It sometimes happens that reputable doctors themselves disagree, in which case there may be a place for investigation by professional writers who specialise in health topics and who research their information conscientiously.

Such documentaries on asbestos, tobacco, herpes or lead are bound to worry some people but, thoughtfully presented, rarely cause patients to stampede to their doctors for the wrong treatment. However, the proper place for bitter debates between doctors over technicalities is in medical meetings and journals and, as far as possible, the public should be protected from them.

The growing preoccupation with ethical issues is a case in point. Their very purpose is to generate worry. Worse still they encourage the growth of a defensive kind of medical practice, in which the best interests of an individual patient cease to be the primary consideration.

An example of this is a television programme about a severely handicapped newborn infant with abnormal chromosomes, a loud heart murmur and intestinal obstruction.

The doctors, relatives and parish priest agree that to perform an operation would be wrong. To enlist the help of a social worker is to invite the risk of interference in the medical management, whereas to conceal the problem from the social services is to deny the family the support they may need. The danger of media medicine is in pressurising individual patients either to seek medical procedures they would do better without, or to avoid treatment they really need. Three very different recent examples readily spring to mind.

The Great Brain Robbery

On October 30, 1980, BBC *Panorama* televised its infamous programme with the title 'Transplants – are the donors really dead?' This emotive title was undoubtedly calculated to draw viewers rather than reassure potential donors. The title conjures up in the imagination scenes of inarticulate patients with their backs to the camera reliving the moments of their deaths; catecholamine over-secreting junior doctors confessing to murder; and earnest pundits pontificating on the ineptitude of everybody else. In reality, this programme was different. One important aspect was that the usual medical authorities for once were conspicuous by their absence, informed medical opinion apparently having been ignored, rejected, refused or so abbreviated as to be unrecognisable.

Four former American patients who had once been declared clinically dead were depicted alive and well. This experience was unreasonably extrapolated to Britain and linked to the unplugging of ventilators to provide spare parts for transplants while the patient still had a reasonable chance of recovery. The programme was ill-timed, almost coinciding with the release of a best-selling novel and

X-certificate film[41] about a chief of surgery who deliberately arranged for his colleagues' operations to go wrong in order to furnish a lucrative private practice in transplants with a steady supply of healthy young organs.

Needless to say, the *Panorama* programme left a trail of protest, antagonism and bad taste. It certainly did nothing to reassure viewers, the distressed relatives of patients on intensive care, or those recently bereaved. Potential donors reputedly tore up their kidney donor cards and in Bristol alone the number of renal transplants was halved in the immediate aftermath of the programme. Deserving patients on chronic renal dialysis who had been waiting for many years were once again disappointed.

The Royal Colleges, the British Medical Association and other responsible bodies were united in their condemnation of the programme. The public had a right to expect discussions on so sensitive an issue to take account of informed medical opinion and to go ahead without it was clearly irresponsible. Much needless anxiety could have been spared on at least two counts: the unfounded allegation that the British criteria of brain death were not reliable and the confusion of two totally separate issues, namely brain death and transplant surgery.

Most patients in coma are not potential donors and the few who are can easily be kept alive until all possible doubt is resolved. The participation of reputable specialists would have clarified the fundamental differences between the American and British criteria and would have left the public not only wiser but more at ease. As an exercise in health education, it was not a success, nor was the unedifying dog-eating-dog wrangle some weeks later. It was not even good television.

---

41. The novel *Coma* by Robin Cook, with film adaption by Michael Crichton.

Pestjahr, 1982

Pestjahr was the word coined by the late Dr Walter Pagel for the year Hitler came to power. It could as easily be used for the year the DHSS[42] launched its campaign of terror promoting whooping cough vaccine. Whooping cough is a disease which unaccountably comes in four-year cycles: 1982 was an epidemic year, as was 1978. In both epidemics, notifications topped around 65,000 in England and Wales, although marginally less last year, despite the relentless knelling of doom.

Notifications in the epidemic and intervening years had previously been much lower, but the uptake of pertussis vaccine had dropped to 30% in the early 1970s when the risk of neurological complications and misgivings about its effectiveness gave the vaccine a bad name. The formulation of the vaccine was therefore changed. The current vaccine is almost certainly safer and more effective and it seems likely that a higher uptake of vaccination for a few years could again bring down the notifications.

What follows, therefore, is not intended as an attack on the current vaccine or its manufacturers but on the crude shock tactics used on the public to promote it by the DHSS.

The campaign began sedately enough with an informative circular to doctors. If only it had continued in this vein it would have been exemplary. Regrettably, with the expected and unavoidable rise in notifications, the DHSS was suddenly galvanised into uncharacteristic hyperactivity. It would be interesting to know how and why the onslaught came to be shifted directly onto the public.

Whooping cough has long ceased to be a serious disease.

---

42. Department of Health and Social Security, the forerunner of the Department of Health.

It is eminently treatable and its mortality in this country has been negligible for over two decades. There were only two notified deaths in England and Wales in the whole of 1972 and only 13 in last year's much-publicised epidemic. They must be seen in the context of measles, which accounts for twice as many cases and four times as many deaths yearly.

Why the outcry about whooping cough when measles is the greater problem? We have an effective vaccine which confers protection for life and could rid this country of measles once and for all in a few years, as has been accomplished in the United States. There are more cot deaths in a week than deaths from whooping cough in a year, not to speak of the many perinatal deaths which could be avoided if the facilities were better. Why the blunderbuss scaremongering over whooping cough?

A fusillade of memoranda, directives and bulletins was unleashed through the media. Having little else to write about since the end of the Falklands campaign, they were only too pleased to join the fray. After all, what is news if it is not bad news? Hardly a day went by without the latest whooping cough returns turning up somewhere. 'KILLER DISEASE STRIKES AGAIN' and 'EPIDEMIC CLAIMS NEW VICTIM' were typical headline messages. Battalions of health visitors and community doctors were thrown into the battle, as if vaccination could conceivably influence notifications or prevent the half-dozen deaths in babies who were too young to be vaccinated anyway. If the aim was to frighten parents out of all proportion, it succeeded, but the worst excess was still to come.

A pre-recorded phone-in service was installed by the DHSS to 'inform' parents about the vaccine. Anybody calling this number was greeted with a blood-curdling series of spasms of coughing, followed by a diatribe on the imminent dangers of brain damage, lung damage and demise. The message ended, like a bad commercial, with a high-pitched hysterical exaltation; 'If your child has not been vaccinated, do not delay. There is an epidemic. Get your child vaccinated now!' This was followed by another paroxysm and what sounded like a last gasp.

At the height of the scaremongering, distraught mothers were telephoning me almost daily. There are over a hundred thousand babies under the age of three months in Britain. If the risks were as great as they were made out to be, what protection was proposed for infants under vaccination age? Some calls came from the mothers of children from whom pertussis vaccine had properly been withheld on sound medical advice. They were worried because they believed their children to be defenceless against a disease on the rampage. They were also worried that the contra-indications to vaccination implied that there was something wrong which they had not been told about.

The whole question of vaccine damage and susceptibility to it is an unresolved inconsistency. Either the vaccine is 100% safe, in which case all normal babies can have it, or it is not, in which case we should not be afraid to say so. The exclusion of a significant number of outwardly normal babies on account of their birth or family histories appears to be a subconscious attempt to shift the onus of responsibility if something goes wrong to the vaccinator instead of the vaccine. A few calls came from parents genuinely worried about possible reactions but even more distressed by the accusations of community doctors or health visitors that their attitude was endangering other people's babies.

As an exercise in health education, the campaign was a mistake. I saw nothing informing the public, or for that matter family doctors, that whooping cough occurs as readily in adults as in children; that natural immunity is short and that the disease can be had repeatedly; that the symptoms of whooping cough can be caused by organisms other than *Bordetella pertussis*; that the vaccine can never be 100% effective or confer more than two or three years of protection; that it could not influence the disease in the community unless adults are vaccinated regularly too; that mild vaccine reactions are common, even if permanent brain damage is mercifully rare; and that to make such a fuss over whooping cough is not being realistic about more important problems concerning child health.

The one message to come across clearly, on a poster, was the awesome '*Whooping Cough is a Killer*'. With 13 deaths and 65,772 survivors this is overstating the case. Nevertheless, television viewers were regaled with the sacrificial vaccinations of some Very Important Little Persons, whose sheltered existence might be expected to render a chance encounter with a *Bordetella pertussis* an unlikely eventuality. Just as the uptake of pertussis vaccine rose from 30% to a modest 45%, a red-faced DHSS ran out of supplies and the campaign of terror came to an abrupt halt. That it had been uncalled for and the cause of much anxiety is beyond dispute. The public should not have been brought into the debate, the whole campaign ought to have been conducted through the profession, and the time spent by countless family doctors and paediatricians on reassurance could have been put to better use.

Breast and Beast

Picture the familiar scene in any labour ward today. Dangling at one end of the baby's waiting cot is a large crudely scrawled sign, which reads 'no milk allowed'.

Some of the mothers have other strong views on pregnancy and labour. They may be squatting on the floor, the room may be in darkness, there may be no fetal monitor, and effective analgesia might have been left until it was too late. The demand on the cot by the mother symbolises an attitude of mind and an unrealistic sense of priority. A sensible mother would prefer to wait until she knows she has a baby who is alive, normal and well. This must be the first priority. She would also be loath to deny a patently hungry baby an occasional bottle-feed.

These strange practices are in my view rarely in the interests of the baby. At least a few are harmed or lost as a result, so where do these implacable views come from? A commonly given pretext by the mother is a history of allergy somewhere in the family. In practice, the children who are destined to develop asthma or eczema do so regardless of how they are fed. It would be more sensible to stop the cleaners sweeping the floor, visitors bringing flowers, banish woolly vests and perfume, and poison all pets. The fear of allergy is really just a put-up excuse.

For once, the media are not primarily responsible but have allowed themselves to become outlets for individuals and groups for whom universal breastfeeding is a religious crusade. In the countries of the Third World, breastfeeding is a necessity. It is not the milk in the bottle which is dangerous, but the ignorance with which it is prepared and the lack of sanitation and clean water. Breastfeeding in the Western World is for mothers and babies who enjoy it; there is no evidence that those who do not are in any way disadvantaged when reared on any of the current modified infant milks. But this is heresy to a crusader for whom any impact on Third World countries depends on Western mothers setting an example, as though this could influence poverty, malnutrition, lack of sanitation, illiteracy or voodoo.

Politically, it seems it is not enough to inform and help our mothers to breastfeed. They must be frightened into doing so and the surest way is to attack and destroy the infant food industry until it no longer offers a possible alternative. Breast is best and beast is beast. Hence the sign at the foot of the cot. The milky crusaders of this world appear unable to extol the virtues of the one without denigrating the other and sowing deep-rooted guilt in their wake.

Every medical student can recite a long list of the advantages of human milk over cow's milk like a catechism. The fact that hardly any of these are relevant to the current modified baby milks is irrelevant. Few students are as well versed in the hazards of feeding fanaticism. Anxiety and depression are again foremost. Probably more fuss and bother is generated over the establishment of lactation than for any other reason in the first few weeks after birth. A vicious cycle is set up so that as the mother becomes more obsessional, the chances of successful lactation diminish. Only those who are not worried by the outcome are almost certain to succeed.

More psychological problems are in store when, 300 sleepless nights later, she tries to wean her breast-addicted baby off the comfort of the breast. In the neonatal period, hypoglycaemia, excessive weight loss and jaundice are potentially serious complications which, if nothing worse, delay the baby's return home. The same is true for premature and low birth weight babies for whom untreated human milk is nutritionally inadequate.

Some babies have lactose intolerance or other metabolic disorders for whom special milk substitutes are essential and the continuation of fanatic breastfeeding could be fatal. Through posters, leaflets, books, classes, political lobbying and a relentless stream of propaganda, the media have allowed themselves to be used.

Prevention

There is no ready solution to the problems of media-induced anxiety, worry, guilt, deprivation or wrongful management. A Code of Information has been suggested but would be difficult to enforce in a free society. If there were such a code, less unsolicited health education from the media and more from patients' own doctors would be a worthy goal.

The Practitioner, September 1983

Britain's first neonatal ambulance, complete
with incubator, resuscitation equipment and a ventilator.
One of Herbert Barrie's greatest achievements.

Dr Herbert Barrie proudly takes delivery of the neonatal
ambulance, pictured here with Sister Hazel Maycock and
Dr Stanley Balfour-Lynn (Variety Club). February 1968.

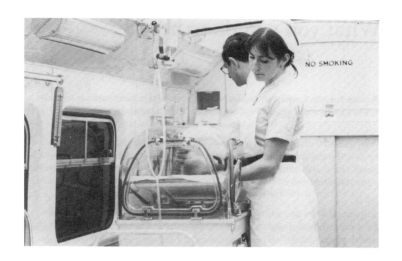

Above and below:
Transporting a premature baby back to the unit.

Herbert Barrie at Charing Cross Hospital, Fulham during visit by Mr (later, Lord) Robert Stewart, MP for Fulham with the Mayor for Fulham in the foreground.

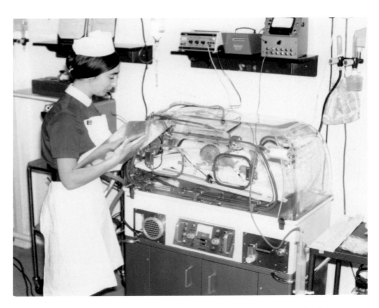

Hazel Maycock, the 'brilliant' sister-in-charge of the unit.

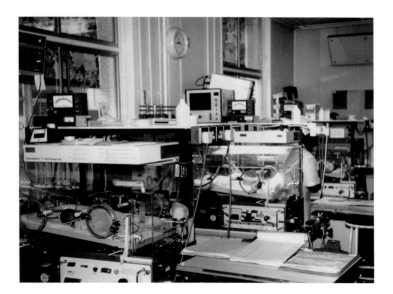

The temporary home of the neonatal unit after it was
damaged by a flood. It was overcrowded and unsafe.

In 1981 Herbert Barrie's neonatal unit moved to a spacious
new site at the West London Hospital. It boasted modern
facilities and state of the art equipment.

Opening of new unit at West London Hospital (part of
Charing Cross Hospital) in July 1981. *From left to right*
Dr Herbert Barrie, Linda Nissim (chairman of Applause)
and Peter Flax (founding member of Young Variety and
the driving force behind the charity for handicapped and
under-privileged children).

Linda Nissim with Michael and Elizabeth Aspel.

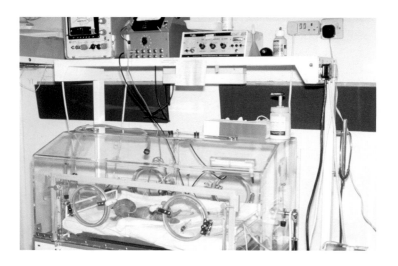

Premature baby in Herbert Barrie's new neonatal unit,
London 1982

Charing Cross Hospital. The Department of Child Health
is the two-storeyed building in the foreground.

Herbert with his children, Caroline and Michael. April 1978.

Herbert with his mother on her birthday, October 1986.

Herbert with his wife, Dinah, and Caroline and Michael.

Herbert Barrie –
circa 1988.

With his
grandsons Robert
(top) in 1996
and Alex (left) in
1999.

Herbert
and Dinah.

Herbert's
wife, Dr
Dinah Barrie
– a consultant
microbiologist.

Herbert was an
accomplished
violinist. He
would, if cajoled,
play to family
and friends.

Herbert was a keen tennis player and was a long-term
member at Coombe Wood Lawn Tennis Club.

Herbert with his daughter-in-law, Roopal.

Christmas Day, 2003.

Herbert with his son, Michael. Christmas Day, 2015.

The Year of the Rat

This is the Year of the Rat. Twenty years ago, researchers found that rats had high blood pressure. Not only was this very common, affecting as many as 50 per cent of rats in some colonies, but it was curiously related to how much salt they ate. Some could eat as much as they liked and did not develop high blood pressure, whereas others did so readily, even if they were given excess salt for only a short time. It was soon possible to breed two strains of rats, salt-sensitive ones who got high blood pressure with salt and salt-resistant ones who did not. A startling finding was the effect of giving too much salt for just a few weeks after birth. The sensitive rats got high blood pressure, even after they were put back on normal food, while those who had only normal food from the start grew up to have normal blood pressures.

What has this to do with us, or, perhaps more specifically, with health visitors and nurses? Hypertension is, of course, one of the major diseases of adult life. One in eight Americans become hypertensive and many eventually die of it. Amazonian Indians do not get it, but in north-eastern Japan, where the salt intake is very high, the incidence of hypertension is one of the highest in the world. A relationship between a high salt intake and high blood pressure is unquestionable. The burning question is whether, like rats, some families are salt-resistant and some are sensitive, and whether hypertensive adults were once children who had too much salt in the first few years of life.

Nutritionists have been concerned for a long time about the high amount of sodium present in cow's milk, compared to breast milk. As a result, baby milks have been modified more and more until now they are as salt-poor as mature breast milk, so much so that some babies do not get enough. A pint of breast milk or a modern baby milk contains just about the right amount of salt a baby needs per day. Those who cannot drink that much, like very premature babies, go short and will not grow unless the difference is made good. Generally speaking, however, the salt intake of breast- and bottle-fed babies has been about right for the last ten years and most of the commonly used commercial weaning foods have been deliberately salt-poor since the early 1970s. If a few had too much salt in the first year, it could only have come from home cooking or from drinking too much cows' milk.

After that, everything becomes much more complicated. Hamburgers, sausages, corned beef, bacon, crisps, peanut butter, salted butter and all kinds of fast foods contain too much salt. The list is endless and one of the worst offenders is the increasingly popular Chinese take-away, which contains enough sodium to last an average adult several days. The link between genetically predisposed school children who eat salty foods and get high blood pressure later remains to be established. But if last year was the Year of the Pig, it is appropriate that in this, the Year of the Rat, we should encourage everyone, adults and children alike, to eat less salt.

Midwife, Health Visitor & Community Nurse, January 1984

Back to Nature

A steady but growing trickle of strange ladies is infiltrating the system and arriving in labour wards up and down the country with a familiar shopping list of demands telling doctors and midwives what to do.[43]

At the top of the list is their insistence that the birth should be 'natural', whatever that means. This year it is having the baby in the squatting position. Last year, it was under water and the year before, in the dark. Next year, it could be hanging from the chandeliers. After thousands of years of human reproduction, the innovative positions women contrive for this basic physiological function is inexhaustible.

They begin by insisting they are perfectly reasonable, flexible people and therefore ask to be kept fully informed throughout. Then follows a long list of dos and don'ts, including procedures to which they would definitely not consent. They do not want the membranes ruptured, for example, nor do they want any fetal monitoring. They do not want to be offered analgesics, pinning all their hope and faith on the 'active participation' of their 'partners', the appearance of some of whom is certainly enough to numb the senses. Should the labour drag on, they do not want it speeded up in the usual way, nor do they want ergometrine used before (sic) or after the baby is born. The baby is not allowed drugs or any treatment, even

---

43. This article was picked up by the press and hit the headlines. Dad appeared on several news items on TV – indeed, there is a clip of such an appearance on YouTube. Dad bemoaned 'birth plans', and although much in vogue throughout the past twenty-five years, the tide is beginning to turn again in favour of recognising the part technology has to play in achieving a safe, risk-free labour.

oxygen, without adequate discussion and their expressed permission in every instance. Instead, they want to deliver the baby themselves and slide it to the breast immediately, preferably with the cord still attached. In the fullness of time, 'partner' cuts the cord and the baby see-saws from the arms of one to the other – who, it must be pointed out, could also be female – in a subdued light and to the strains of folk music. They eventually get bored with this and the baby may then be cleaned, dressed and put into a cot, but only on the strictest understanding that it is never, ever, under any circumstances, given a bottle. Should the labour unfortunately end in a stillbirth, the procedure is exactly the same only more so. The couple must be given every consideration to grieve for a death which could have been avoided with proper treatment, and the staff should take a few pictures of the body to facilitate the process as, for some reason, this is not something that the parents, relatives or undertaker could reasonably be expected to do themselves. However, the possibility that the baby might not be normal is never entertained, and it is axiomatic of natural childbirth that deformed babies never happen.

What is one to make of all this? Speaking as a paediatrician, I would just as soon have nothing to do with these people; I want a live, healthy baby, with clear air passages and well-expanded lungs. The obstetrician is up against a more difficult problem. These patients tend to arrive, without warning, in the labour ward with their lethal shopping lists. As adults, they are within their rights to reject professional advice for themselves, even if this does expose the baby to greater risk. But they are not entitled to tell doctors how to do their work. They are not entitled to ask us to lower professional standards and to jeopardise babies' lives.

The temptation is to send them home and leave it all to the general practitioner, but this is hardly fair on him, the midwife, or the baby. If we accept that this is a free country – which it is – and that people have a right to choose how they have their babies, we must retain the right to stick to our professional standards. There are vast stretches of wilderness on this earth where you would not find a doctor or fetal monitor within a thousand miles. Those who want a natural birth in the bush should go there.

Faculty News, October 1984

The Breast-Addicted Baby

This story is all too familiar. It is also very contemporary. The mother, usually endowed with more education than sense, loses her maternal instinct in the brain wash-tub of the antenatal classes. Most antenatal teachers are eminently respectable and beyond reproach, but a few of a certain breed are terrible. This mother, of course, has to try several until she finds one bad enough. During labour, and long before she knows whether her baby is normal or will live, she dangles a tell-tale sign on the empty waiting cot: 'NO BOTTLES ALLOWED' or, nonsensically, 'WATER ONLY'. The next few days in an open ward are spent topless in Gaza, like hanging out the washing when it is dry, while hospital porters and floor cleaners go about their business, unimpressed. Luckily for most babies, milk starts to flow and compulsive feeding can then make up for lost ounces. A few less lucky ones are condemned to starve longer, evidenced by a falling weight and a mounting pile of baby books and canned beer on the mother's locker, as if milk production were subject to the same influences as diuresis or verbal diarrhoea.

At home, the saga continues with two-hourly and even hourly feeds. The two important prerequisites in any state of addiction are the addict and the pusher – the one weak and acquiescent, the other persistent and exploiting. It must be shared, the needs of the one preying on the dependence of the other. It is difficult to say whether it begins with a hungry baby demanding frequent feeds until there is sufficient milk but continuing to take only a little at a time; or whether it is the mother who has to put the baby on the breast every ten minutes, as a result of which the baby only takes small volumes. Whatever the reason, a characteristic pattern of mothercare and infant behaviour is likely to follow. Because the baby is fed from ten to twenty times a day, she carries him around most of the time, slung round her neck in a special harness, and rarely puts him down. Inevitably, feeding takes place at every opportunity as the baby becomes increasingly adept in accomplishing the three-inch journey, and barriers part with increasing facility. Sooner or later, the breast becomes a dummy as well as a source of food, and our baby is hooked.

By this time, the fact that the baby is almost continually on or near the breast is inescapable, particularly in public places or when the baby is disturbed as in clinics or surgeries. He cries when he is put down, is sometimes sick, keeps his parents awake at night and nobody else can have him, but still there is no problem. It all depends on what his mother does about weaning. If she does nothing, then by the age of six months, the baby is so habituated that any change is difficult and by nine months, Herculean. He – or equally, she – refuses any comfort other than the breast. The noise level he can register when frustrated is truly formidable at close range, and sometimes culminates into a fully blown breath-holding attack. He has erupted several sharp teeth and is too heavy to carry slung round in front any longer. He has moved into his mother's bed at night and bitter arguments develop over how the situation should be handled, with the grandmothers joining in. Nobody else can satisfy this unique craving. The baby is totally dependent on the mother for each fix and every time she gives him one she makes it more difficult for herself to deny the next. The frenzied violence and desperate urgency of an acute withdrawal have to be seen to be believed. Terrifying screams reaching ever new heights of fever pitch continue relentlessly, and the child is obviously distressed, flushed, sweating, hot, trembling and sick, plus the certain knowledge that the breast will always bring instant relief, peace and forgiveness. Anyone who has ever witnessed a nine-months-old toddler in the full throes of a withdrawal will at once recognise the unmistakeable symptoms and signs of cold turkey.

The treatment – sedation and strong nerves – is basically the same. There the similarity ends because breast addiction is self-limiting. As is the way of all flesh, normal babies eventually grow tired of this particular form of solace, just as others do with bottles, dummies, dishcloths and bits of blanket. It could take years, as certain appurtenances can more easily be lost irretrievably than others. It may leave a trail of disaster but fortunately few mothers make the same mistake a second time.

Faculty News, April 1985

Too Small and Too Soon

The most important single reason for the current shortage of neonatal intensive care cots is the enormous amount of time and effort spent on infants who were born too small and too soon. To anyone who has experienced the frustration of trying to transfer a critically ill baby to the nearest special care unit, the story has a familiar ring; it is not that the unit staff are unsympathetic or unwilling, but with several babies, all still under 1,000g, there is no chance of accepting any more for several weeks.

A 900g baby of 26 weeks' gestation who makes good progress is still likely to weigh under 1,000g at one month and can expect to remain in the unit for many months at enormous cost. Ten years ago, survival for more than a few days was exceptional. Today, the survival of babies of ever-decreasing size and maturity is spurred on by the unrealistic expectation of the public that all babies should survive no matter how small or imperfect. When a perfectly viable baby is denied special care so that those of dubious viability should linger, the time has come to ask ourselves: how small is too small?

According to the *Guinness Book of Records*, the smallest known survivor was born in South Shields in 1938 weighing 10 ounces (238g) and was reputedly fed by her GP every hour with a fountain pen. If still alive, she would now be nearing her fiftieth birthday. Nothing quite so small has yet been claimed in contemporary neonatal intensive care, but a full account appeared last year of a girl who was born in a Pennsylvania community hospital at 25 and a half weeks' gestation and who weighed only 15½oz (440g). She was moved to a nearby intensive care unit after two days and had surprisingly few complications. Two years later, she weighed 12kg and was developmentally normal.

Isolated success stories are exciting, but it is important not to lose sight of the fate of the majority of very low birth weight babies. Firstly, there is a wide difference between those over 1,000g and 27 weeks, and those below. This is a critical watershed which has altered little after two decades. Certainly the chances of survival under 1,000g are substantially better than they were, but successes cling closely to the 900g line and the failures rise relentlessly under 850g. Twenty years of technological progress achieved a reduction of some ten days in maturity and 150g in weight. Thereafter, the mortality rises relentlessly. It exceeds 50 per cent in the best centres, and of the survivors, over 50 per cent can be expected to be moderately or severely handicapped.

Cranial ultrasound scans in the first few days show brain haemorrhages in over 60 per cent, and of sufficient severity in at least a third to result in permanent disability. Beside brain damage there are many other hurdles to overcome, not least of which is a form of lung fibrosis leading to months of dependency on extra oxygen.

The unpalatable truth is that the lower limit of viability has changed only marginally despite considerable endeavour, although the outlook for those on or near it is better. It would be unrealistic to expect any further lowering in the foreseeable future. The demand of the public and enthusiasm of the profession for breaking records is rarely shared by the parents who are usually young and for whom a severely handicapped child is a catastrophe. Confronted with the personal problems of the smallest of the small, they may be forgiven for wishing secretly that the doctors and nurses would not try so hard. We should talk less of salvage and concern ourselves from now on with intact survival.

Midwife, Health Visitor & Community Nurse, October 1985

Bonding Debunked

GPs and others – especially others – can put their brushes away and give their glue-pots a well-earned rest. Baby-bonding, codswallop of the decade, has finally joined the club of has-beens like floating kidneys, winkle-picker footwear and the little bits of plastic people stuck on the bonnets of their cars to ward off flies. Even psychologists have long ceased to believe in baby-bonding. Gail Ross pooh-poohed the idea five years ago, followed by Lamb (1982), the Sluckins (1983) and now Martin Richards (1985), not to speak of my own contribution in 1976. I then said it was an affront to common sense and out of touch with the realities of labour wards and special care baby units. Neither Ross nor Lamb were convinced that holding or not holding the baby immediately after birth had anything whatsoever to do with being a good or a bad mother, and both thought it created anxieties where none previously existed. The Sluckins believe the hocus-pocus of bonding, as practised by some doctors and nurses, has a lot to answer for and evidently spend much of their time undoing the mischief. To Richards, the notion of bonding has become a positive block to understanding the needs of mothers and babies, and the sooner we forget about it, the sooner we can begin to make some real progress.

That the vast majority of mothers and fathers cherish their children, and a tiny minority do not, has never been in dispute – only the far-fetched notion that this is something in the remit of doctors and nurses to switch on or off at will. It began with claims of a psychologically critical first few minutes in a baby's life when close contact with the mother and father was vital 'for later development to be optimal'. If babies were not glued to their parents and allowed to set, like two bits of wood, the consequences were dire indeed, from burps to baby bashing, brain damage and death. The evidence came from safaris to monkey houses, sheep farms and duck ponds, plus observations on a small number of unrepresentative mothers indulging their babies in what most people would call a cuddle but which came to be known throughout the world as 'extended skin contact'.

Like a woman's charm, if you had it, you needed nothing else; and if you did not have it, it mattered little else you had. Bonding became the all-consuming passion of countless midwives, nurses, social workers, do-gooders and hangers-on, not to speak of a few gullible doctors. In the temples of our antenatal clinics, posters of bare mothers and babies gazed down pinkly, enduring hypothermia. Eye-to-eye and navel-to-navel contact became the order of the day before the placenta was out. Mothers and babies – but few fathers – shared beds to the discomfort of the one and peril of the other. Breastfeeding was urged not for the food but for the bonding. Mothers carried their babies slung round their necks all the time, even to the bathroom, not because there was a shortage of cots but for a mystical – and mythical – harmony of heartbeats. Those who had caesarean sections had intensive superglue, as did mothers of babies in incubators. The obsession with bonding knew no respect for size and one saw babies hardly the size of one's hand lifted from the safety of incubators for regular doses of adhesive as long as they survived the treatment.

Ten years and dozens of projects later, the bonding business lies debunked. The original work had numerous flaws and nobody had been able to reproduce the results, although not for want of trying. There is overwhelming evidence that you cannot attach a baby to a mother who does not want one, or detach one from a mother who does. That a critical period of skin-to-skin or toe-to-toe contact is bunkum is good news for thousands of successful adoptive parents who managed perfectly well without; and tens of thousands whose babies were saved by special care after days or weeks of separation; and hundreds of thousands of proud dads who were not around when the baby arrived, or if they were, drew the line at skin-to-tattoo contact through bashfulness, modesty, urgent business or the fear of getting covered in wee-wee or meconium.

The epoxy epidemic is finally over. All that remains is to find a resting place for the word 'bonding'. Personally, I should like to see it erased from the medical vocabulary and returned to the shelves of hardware shops where it belongs.

Faculty News, November 1985

How to be a Natural Father

It takes leadership, constancy, and an elastic sense of fun!

If the business of mothercraft basks in the perpetual glow of publicity, fathercraft keeps a traditionally low profile. Most men vaguely know what it is about and take a back seat for fear of treading on female preserves.

The fact is, the average British dad is a retiring sort of chap who is frankly terrified of mothers and babies in great number, which to him means more than three of each at any one time. If you want to see a picture of abject and discomfited paternity, you do not have to go further than the local playschool when it is Father's turn to take the toddler.

Or, one better, you could try the antenatal preparation class to which a first-time father can often be induced to go once and where, with the famous upper lip and gritted teeth, he may be seen in an unaccustomed position on a cushion on the floor between rows of vastly pregnant women, trying hard not to see the generous breastfeeding propaganda on the walls. This is a time for red faces, necks and ears and possibly one reason why the few who stay the course always seem to have big bushy beards and long hair.

The long neglect of fathercraft can partly be attributed to the way it is muddled up with mothercraft. It is assumed that when a father shows a little interest, he must want to know all about childbirth, squatting or otherwise, bathing the baby or changing nappies.

There is, of course, absolutely nothing wrong in getting fathers to bath babies or powder bottoms any more than washing dishes or cooking breakfast. What is wrong is for strange professionals to teach him how. In normal families, it is part and parcel of good mothering for mothers to acquire the skills and to pass them on to willing fathers who should have the good sense not to try to better their instructors. High-class chefs know better than to supervise home cooking.

The first rule of good fathercraft is to be *helpful* and supportive, in other words good husbands. One can often see good and bad omens at the time of birth. A good sign is when the father-about-to-be stays at the head of the bed and generally tries to be helpful; or who, by mutual agreement and at the crucial moment, waits patiently outside. A bad sign is when the father forbids effective pain relief, as if it is any of his business; or shows an anatomic interest in every stage of labour, shouting, 'Push!' louder and more enthusiastically than anyone else; who has views on severing the umbilical cord in person; or who dashes around frantically making a video film of the event from beginning to end from the only clinical vantage points possible.

Few children would want to see a video film of their own birth, let alone invite their school friends along for the show. But then, children cannot choose their parents. If only they could, there would be many more perfect parents. As it is, not only do children have no choice but when it comes to fathers, many never know what it is to have one.

Children, who have an uncanny insight on such matters, would rate *constancy* high among the qualities of the perfect father. Constancy means regularity, faithfulness, steadfastness and reliability. Children are more easily abandoned by their fathers than by mothers, and this is a fact of life they meet or at least sense from a very early age.

The best of fathers must leave and return every day, and there is nothing like a period of absence to encourage appreciation, quite apart from the lurking fear that he might never come back. There are substitutes, many of them admirable, but abandonment is a particularly hard cross to bear. As one five-year-old put it, 'I've got three daddies, which is nice on birthdays but not at other times.'

Third on the list of special qualities is *gratitude*. Being a parent implies years of giving with little in return and one must learn to be grateful for what little there is. The same self-sacrifice is required also of mothers, but whereas they must put their children first, fathers are proverbially expected to put mother and children first.

The biggest trap today is to forget all about self-sacrifice and gratefulness for small mercies, and to regard the pleasures to be had from normal children as a divine right. This is particularly evident when the needs of children have to take second place.

Here at least our perfect father can set a good example. If the baby cries, as commonly happens, and the mother becomes tearful, as is equally common, the obvious trap is for father to rush around aggressively, looking for someone to blame, instead of exerting a calming influence. Mothers who worry over nothing are enough trouble without fathers joining in.

But what if there really is something to worry about? Nothing can be more testing for a father's qualities of *leadership* and *understanding*. A common enough occurrence is the birth of a baby with some flaw. How many fathers would say it made no difference?

Another desirable virtue in fathers is an elastic sense of fun. The perfect father cannot be an age-group specialist, great when it comes to minding the nursery and a dab hand with bottle-feeding, but useless at swimming at five, football at 10 or fishing at 15 years. Being a good father does not begin and end in the delivery room. It goes on for years, changing gradually but with a deepening companionship the full extent of which may not be appreciated until after the children have left home.

It takes all sorts to make a world and inevitably one meets the best and the worst and a whole lot in between. A good one who fell into a trap but redeemed himself nobly was a young man who misread the homely features of the birth attendants and jumped to the conclusion that there was something seriously amiss. Although the baby was perfectly normal, the midwife did not actually say so to him, only to his wife. This confirmed his worst fears that some terrible news was being withheld from him.

Three days went by when it became obvious to everybody that his poor wife had no cards, telegrams, flowers or visitors for the simple reason that he had not told anybody in case the baby did not live. A crash course in fathercraft which took less than ten minutes produced the desired effect before the day was out – half a flower shop, two dozen greetings cards, two bottles of champagne, innumerable telephone calls and a diamond ring. It may not be everybody's choice of a name, but as the baby was a girl, they called her... Desiree.

The Best of Health Magazine, 1986

Charing Cross Hospital (Fulham)
Fulham Palace Road, London W6 8RF
Department of Paediatrics

Miss Sue Douet   27 March 1986
Director of Nursing Services
Charing Cross Hospital

Dear Sue,

I hate having to pressurise you but I need your categorical reassurance that nurses may not refer hospital patients to a social worker against medical advice. It goes without saying that the views of the ward staff are always welcome and highly regarded, but I must be absolutely firm on this issue.

I am concerned not only with the good of my own patients but, as physician-in-charge of the Department, I have to provide an inpatient service in which all consultants who use the paediatric wards – especially the orthopaedic and neurosurgeons – have complete confidence. I simply cannot allow a situation in which nurses hand over medical records or divulge their contents without permission, or worse still, make the relatives see the social worker who inevitably appears on the ward when the consultant has already told them they are under no obligation to do so.

I want you to make it clear to your staff that the decision to involve a social worker is a clinical one and may not be made by nurses acting against medical advice.

Yours sincerely,
Herbert Barrie
Consultant Paediatrician
Head of Department of Child Health

Pertussis and the Wolf

The much-heralded epidemic of whooping cough is here. Previous outbreaks have recurred at intervals of three to four years. Since the last in 1982, nobody has been allowed to forget that the next could be expected in 1985/86, on the principle that the greater the public apprehension the greater the vaccine uptake. Like the Ides of March, the time may have come but not yet gone and notifications are likely to stay up until the end of the year. Nevertheless, a few tentative conclusions can be drawn.

Firstly, there can be little doubt that whooping cough vaccine is effective in reducing notifications both between and during epidemics. An immediate effect on the peaks and troughs was seen when widespread vaccination began in 1957. Equally noticeable has been the resurgence of the disease with the drop in vaccine uptake from 80% in 1968 to 30% in 1976. The present uptake nationally is about 65% and, according to epidemiologists, at least 80% is needed to make any major inroads into the prevalence of an infectious disease. If the current epidemic is not as great as pessimists had prophesised, what are we to conclude? Is it that a lower acceptance rate is adequate? Or is it that the worst is still to come? Or is it that the disease is diminishing anyway?

In the case of whooping cough, notifications are at best only a crude indication of its incidence. They thrive on heightened publicity and decline at times of disinterest. They say nothing about severity. Laboratory proof is usually missing so that numerous cases are reported wrongly, just as many others which should be reported are not.

What is clear is that the duration of immunity to this particular infection lasts only a few years, as can be inferred from its three- to four-year cycles, and that every population must have enormous reservoirs of susceptible adults.

There can be little doubt that adults with whooping cough exist and can be found by those who care to look. They may not whoop like children but they still spread the disease, perhaps even more than children, and the wholesale vaccination of children cannot hope to eradicate the disease until adults are regularly given the vaccine too.

Fortunately, there are signs that the disease has become milder over the years for many reasons, of which vaccination is only one. The repeated and heartless assertion that whooping cough is an indiscriminate killer and bringer of brain damage is simply no longer true in this country. Forty years ago, the mortality might have been more than 1% but in the outbreak of 1982, there were only 14 deaths in 65,810 notified cases – a mortality rate of one in 5,000. Last year, there were four deaths among 21,483 reported cases. Furthermore, the few deaths have not been analysed and may have been complicated by social factors and other illnesses.

Whichever way one looks at it, the reassuring fact emerges that the chances of survival are excellent and, indeed, overwhelmingly superior to crossing the road (2,000 annual child deaths from accidents) or being born (2,500 avoidable perinatal deaths annually).

An official DHSS press release in September 1982 gave the risk of an unvaccinated child contracting the disease as between one in 16 and one in 30. With a vaccine acceptance of 65% and a population of close on three million children under the age of five years in the UK, this is clearly a considerable overstatement.

So far, the epidemic has mercifully been disappointing, at least to the prophets of doom. Notifications in Greater

London, a city of no mean size, have rarely exceeded 100 per week since September and actually fell to 20 after Christmas. At least one London borough, and with the lowest vaccine uptake at that, has had only 15 reported cases in six months. Puzzled general practitioners may well ask: Where's the epidemic? Crying wolf is not the answer.

The Practitioner, May 1986

The Epoxy Plague

The existence of a bond between parents and children has never been in dispute; it is the bizarre notion that this bond can be permanently damaged by a minor event or made to flourish by the trivial intercession of nurses and doctors which has caused much controversy. The idea that there exists a process which birth attendants have the power to light up or extinguish at will has at last been discredited.

At the heart of the baby-bonding hypothesis is the extraordinary claim that: '...there is a sensitive period in the first minutes or hours of life during which it is necessary that the mother and father have close contact with their neonate for later development to be optimal'. In other words, whatever feelings the mother and father may have for their baby, everything depends on what happens in the first few minutes after the birth. Parents and baby are required to spend the first hour together in naked solitude, eye to eye and skin to skin, until the hypothetical glue has set.

This hypothesis became increasingly elaborate as it became clothed in a thin and threadbare coat of pseudo-scientific jargon. The first 30 to 60 minutes were claimed to be special because the magic love potion was then at its most potent. At no other time is the baby more appealing or are the parents more highly charged. The baby, eyes wide open, sees the mother's face, hears her voice and responds rhythmically to her words '...in a beautiful linking and synchronised dance. This broad array of sensory and motor abilities evoke responses from the mother and begin the communication which may be especially helpful for attachment and the initiation of a series of reciprocal interactions. Keeping the mother and baby together soon after birth is likely to initiate and enhance the operation of sensory, hormonal, physiological, immunological and behavioural mechanisms that help lock the parent to the infant.'

The consequences of the disruption of this process were apparently dire: the mother-child relationship could never be the same. Mothers who neglected the 'ritual of the skins' loved their babies less and could not look after them properly. The babies were not breastfed for as long, if at all. They cried more and failed to thrive. They walked and talked later and had lower IQs. They had more psychological problems and developed the 'vulnerable child syndrome', whatever that is. They had more accidents. Last of all – but not least – some babies were rejected and neglected. Battered babies were unbonded babies, separation at birth marking the beginning of a process of deprivation which would stretch into generations.

Of the many flaws in the baby-bonding hypothesis, one of the more interesting is the fact that no practising obstetrician or midwife has so far become accidentally bonded to a baby whose naked skin he or she has held and into whose limpid eyes he or she has gazed at the crucial time. Obstetricians and labour ward staff who regularly assist at deliveries have been conspicuously disinterested in the idea of bonding. The most ardent followers have been nurses, teachers and social workers, who have relatively little practical experience of labour wards.

The experience of thousands of babies and their families indicates that mothers, fathers, grandparents and siblings forge strong and lasting links with a new baby without undergoing any ritualistic rigmaroles. Similarly, the evidence of thousands of adoptive parents, foster parents and even nannies shows that separation is no bar to enduring affection and attachment. There is also the evidence of families with twins and triplets which makes a nonsense of the bonding myth and its dependence on prolonged eye-gazing or breastfeeding. A particularly outstanding example is the justly famous family of sextuplets – the only surviving group in the world – whose survival was only made possible by prolonged intensive care and artificial feeding.

The weakness of the bonding theory is its exaggeration of the importance of a few fleeting moments, whilst ignoring all preceding and subsequent events. This is especially true of neonatal intensive care. The overwhelming evidence from extensive practical experience is that babies who survive a difficult birth tend to be precious, and therefore treasured all the more. Neonatologists and neonatal unit nursing staff have been encouraged to find that the most seriously ill babies are commonly given even more care and attention by their parents than those who have never been ill. The issue of the effects of separation caused by admission to special care baby units has become confused with issues relating to a higher proportion of unwanted pregnancies, congenital abnormalities, handicap and socio-economic factors in premature labour. The idea that maternal rejection is an inevitable consequence of placing the baby in an incubator is naive and facile. One in five births are complicated and one in ten babies require resuscitation or admission to a special care baby unit. Therefore, separation is a common event, whereas child abuse is mercifully not. As childbirth is becoming safer and more humane, child abuse is getting worse instead of better, along with delinquency, crime and violence. This decline in moral values can hardly be blamed on midwives or the third stage of labour.

Behavioural psychologists, initially sympathetic to the miracle-glue concept, became disillusioned when they found they could not reproduce the results; they are now its greatest antagonists. Other investigators found serious flaws in the design of the studies on baby-bonding. The mothers chosen were unrepresentative of the general population, the numbers were too small, the criteria used to indicate good mothering had little to do with good or bad mothering, and too many hasty conclusions were drawn from the flimsiest of findings. There was only one consistently reproducible finding – that which showed no significant difference in the long term between the mothers and babies who had had close contact and those who had not.

Gail Ross, in an academic analysis of the whole subject of parental attachment, was one of the first to cast doubt on the relevance of early contact to human behaviour. She concluded that 'claims of a sensitive period for bonding and a biological basis of attachment are not borne out by empirical evidence, and long-lasting effects of early and extended mother-infant contact have not yet been demonstrated. Mother-infant attachment is not an all-or-none event but an unfolding developing process'.

Lamb reviewed all the studies on bonding and was forced to conclude that the bonding theory was not based on scientifically sound evidence. He wrote: 'Emphasis on the critical importance of bonding has created a legion of parents who feel that they have missed something terribly important and thus can never be as competent or nurturant as those parents who were able "to bond". The effects of such feelings of guilt or failure may be more significant than the demonstrated positive effects of early contact.'

In 1983, Sluckin, Herbert and Sluckin, specialists in family guidance, published a book on maternal bonding based on their own work with mothers and babies. They pointed out the importance of cultural differences and were concerned by the many mothers who were made needlessly anxious by the thoughtless suggestion that they might not be properly 'bonded'. Whether a particular mother strokes or does not stroke her baby depends on her cultural background. English mothers are more likely to do so than Spanish mothers, while in some Asian communities mothers are considered unclean for up to three days after delivery, and intimate contact between mother and baby is frowned on. The process of bonding as encouraged by some midwives then becomes an unwanted harassment. The authors concluded: 'Carefully conducted follow-up studies of mothers show that perinatal events, including skin-to-skin contact or its absence, do not determine mother-to-infant attachment, mother love or maternal care-giving skills. Those who give advice to young mothers can help them best by focusing on the present and on the future, rather than by dwelling on perinatal events which cannot be undone and which, as we now know, are far less influential than often believed.'

Martin Richards (1985) also finds the notion of bonding unacceptable, the cause of much needless anxiety and a positive block to progress. The idea that human relationships can be upset by a single event runs counter to what we know about adaptability and compensation. It makes us ignore the world from which parents come and to which they return with their baby. It gives a distorted view of the nature of developmental processes and ignores the complexities of human relationships.

It has been said that, for all its faults, the focus on bonding has at least made labour wards and nurseries kinder places. My personal view is that these changes were destined to occur anyway, along with more enlightened attitudes to health care generally, from childhood to old age. Effective pain relief has done more than anything else to emancipate labour wards from their one-time image, while active life-saving treatments have changed the masterly inactivity holy-of-holies face of special care baby units. Attitudes began to change long before the 'epoxy plague' began and have continued to change despite it.

In my opinion, bonding has done more harm than good. The preoccupation of midwives, nurses and a few doctors with bonding was far too often used as an excuse for neglecting more important and more difficult matters. Far from being just another harmless fad, giving rise to a little anxiety here and there, the uncritical enthusiasm for baby-bonding seriously undermined standards of proper neonatal care and took its inevitable toll. The bonding plague, now mercifully over, carried a mortality which is impossible to estimate but which, at its height, probably exceeded in one year the combined deaths from whooping cough and measles in Britain in the last 30 years.

It is both urgent and vital that all midwives and nurses who have not already done so try to put the bonding myth behind them and eradicate the word 'bonding' from their medical vocabularies forever. There is overwhelming evidence that you cannot stick a baby to a mother who does not want it or unstick one from a mother who does. Not even after 50 years.

Maternal and Child Health, October 1986

Mumbo Gumbo

The history of childbirth is littered with more than its fair share of flotsam and jetsam from passing whims. Thankfully, baby-bonding is on its way out. This is good tidings at a time when the birth and love of the newborn child has special meaning for so many people.

A slavish pre-occupation with the doctrine has done more harm than good. Mothers have been unthinkingly harassed, babies put unnecessarily at risk and the conduct of the third stage of a labour wrongly and ludicrously blamed for the growing evil of child abuse. Now that the end is in sight, millions of ordinary mothers and fathers, who never felt a need or urge for the bizarre rituals without which, so it was said, their babies could not grow up 'optimally', can relax.

It must bring comfort and relief to those who have successfully adopted or fostered countless numbers of unwanted children months if not years after they were born. Mothers who have their babies by caesarean section, or in circumstances making separation unavoidable, can stop feeling guilty and inadequate and take heart that, in the years to come, it really does not matter. So can fathers who, perhaps just as well, display little enthusiasm for early skin contact in labour wards; and the soldiers and sailors of this world whose babies arrive while they are far away. Brothers, sisters, grandparents and all the other doting relatives do not have to do anything special anymore to be able to love the new arrival. The parents of twins, triplets or quads, for whom applications of miracle-glue always posed formidable anatomical difficulties, can be left to enjoy their good fortune in peace.

Henceforth, apnoeic[44] babies who, at one time, were in danger of being 'bonded' before they could be revived, may now be resuscitated first without question. No baby need be chilled in the cause of early skin contact, or lack oxygen or glucose. The hungry will not be denied milk or the jaundiced phototherapy for the sake of a little mum-gum. Those in need of special care must have it. The precarious lives of very ill and very premature babies should no longer be put in jeopardy by taking them out of their incubators when they would be far safer left unmolested, or by moving them into cots before they are fit, or by sending them home weeks too soon. An excuse for carelessness is tempting, but high standards of medical and nursing care are never incompatible with treating babies and their families with gentleness and consideration.

The doctrine of baby-bonding gained its noisome and uncritical support from those mostly outside labour wards. It never had the blessing of most responsible obstetricians, neonatologists or labour ward staff. Now that it has also been rejected uncompromisingly by most responsible psychologists, there is no earthly reason why midwives, nurses and teachers should continue to pay lip-service to a mischievous and out-dated concept.

Midwife, Health Visitor & Community Nurse, December 1986

---

44. No longer breathing.

Feeding Premature Babies

The survival of very low birth weight babies is one of the outstanding success stories of the last ten years. A few babies as small as 500g have been kept alive by a combination of bewildering technology, tender loving care and dedicated teamwork.

It is a long, hard and perilous haul before premature babies are ready for home, and when they are, they are still considerably below the average size and weight of a normal term baby.

While in hospital, the aim is to get babies to grow as fast as possible so they can go home in the shortest possible time. Once home, putting on weight rapidly is no longer a top priority as long as they thrive, and a modest, steady weight gain is perfectly all right.

Unfortunately, this simple truth is easily befogged by breast milk politics. Breast milk is not designed for the fastest growth of preterm babies. Small babies fed exclusively on fresh expressed breast milk either stay in hospital longer or weigh less on going home.

How Much Milk?

The great milk debate need not concern us here since all agree that, once preterm babies are home, there is no objection to breastfeeding. The mother's output should rarely present any problems since small babies require very little milk. The magic formula is 3oz per pound per day (2½oz for a term baby).

In metrics this comes to 180ml per kg per day (150ml for term babies). A 2.5kg baby needs 2.5 x 180ml of milk daily by breast or bottle in order to gain approximately 30g or 1oz a day.

It is important to remember that to grow an ounce of body tissue requires exactly the same building materials at 5 lb weight as at 10 lb. These materials – protein, fat, minerals, and so on – are only just contained in the average amount of milk which a contented term baby takes in a typical day. A baby of only half the normal size takes only half the daily quantity and therefore only half the necessary building materials.

There are only three ways round this – either to use a stronger milk, give double helpings or accept a slower rate of growth. The first two options happen in special care baby units where they can be carefully controlled. The compromise option is what happens at home.

Even so, the daily requirement – 3oz or 90ml per pound per day – is quite a bellyful for the GI tract of a small baby. Few can manage what a term baby takes in one go, so that the smaller the baby, the smaller the feeds and the shorter the intervals between them.

Mothers desperately keen to take their four-pounder home – which, in my view, is unacceptably small – would have to provide a feed at least every three hours day and night for several weeks.

In practice, the feeding of premature babies allowed home is rarely a problem, and a more respectable discharge weight of at least 5 lb helps. The only requirement is milk in smaller amounts, but more often.

The advantages of bottle-feeding are that the mother knows how much goes in and others can share the work, but provided the baby is contended and gains steadily, the actual intake is academic.

Fully breast-fed babies should be weighed weekly at first

and gain at least 5 – 6oz (150 – 180g) a week, and this is where health visitors can be towers of strength and support.

Test-Weighing at Home

Test-weighing, i.e., weighing the clothed baby before and after a feed, is unnecessary unless there is a serious doubt about the output of milk. It needs accurate scales because one is trying to measure only a few ounces, and weighing should be repeated a few times since a single measurement may not reflect what happens at other feeds. Try using a plastic washing-up bowl on kitchen scales on a carpeted floor.

Breast-fed babies need a supplement of vitamins and iron; bottle-fed babies probably get enough from the supplements already in the formula, but a little extra would do no harm. The baby milk should be of the modified kind in which there is more soluble protein than casein, as in breast milk.

A few weeks later, when the weight and size are those of any normal term baby, feeding those who were once premature is no different from normal.

Pulse, February 1987

Birthday Honours

The Most Excellent Order of the British Empire (OBE) is the accolade given to both men and woman on the occasion of the Queen's birthday for meritorious service to the Queen and Country and the Empire that was. The award was also something administered no less ceremoniously by midwives to women before labour, and its acronym lingers on, lending a certain poignancy to those famous words: 'Close your eyes and think of England!'

Oil (castor), bath and enema, with a shave thrown in for good measure, came to be identified with the *bête noire* banner of the liberation movement of mothers-to-be, like the burning bras of liberated mothers mostly not-to-be 10 years earlier. In all the excitement, two simple facts were lost or forgotten: firstly, OBEs (for better or worse) were nursing procedures, instigated and inflicted by nurses, and secondly, OBEs ceased to be routine procedures over a quarter of a century ago – in fact, ever since obstetricians (who happen to be predominantly male) found better ways of inducing labour. It is possible that it still rarely happens to someone, somewhere, but to go on ululating about OBEs is like asking to be liberated from blood-letting and leeches.

Of course, anti-interventionists hate induction in any shape or form, which is a pity because there comes a time when apples are ready for picking and only get bruised if allowed to fall. The long hit list includes rupturing the membranes, fetal monitoring, epidurals, episiotomy, ergometrine, oxytocin, caesarean section, clamping the cord, vitamin K, and cow's milk. Childbirth has never been a dignified business, and the rebellion is partly about not taking it lying down any more. 'Squatters, arise and do not be counted!' is the strange new battle cry. Unfortunately, all the alternative postures – and it takes the ingenuity of pregnant women to invent new ones each year – are infinitely less decorous.[45] Effective pain relief is one of the great contributions for the liberation of women during childbirth, offering comfort and a semblance of elegance to labour, as Queen Victoria was quick to recognise. It is difficult to understand why it should be so shunned by a determined few.

Fashions come and go. This has been the year of the beanbag on the floor. Last year, it was squatting and the year before, kneeling. Previous to that, it was having your baby under water or in the dark. We have seen Michelin-type suits and hearkened to the alien strains of ethnic eurythmics. In the great gate of Sanchi, the birth of the Buddha is depicted with the mother hanging from the branches of a tree and the tusk of an elephant. As Newton discovered, what goes up must come down.

Nobody has ventured to have a baby on the moon so far, but the time cannot be far off. With the perinatal mortality down to single figures, perhaps we can afford to take chances. However, for those of us who have seen it all, natural childbirth has an appalling record. There are

---

45. Dad blasted the 'natural childbirth' movement and was emphatic in his criticism. But, as in many things, his concerns were based on medical facts and time has proved him right. Only recently, Patrick O'Brien, a senior obstetrician in London, commented that 'in India and Africa thousands of women with potential complications give birth at home without support because they have no choice, and it ends in disaster. But in the West, childbirth has become so safe that people have just about forgotten that there can be major problems. It's been written out of people's psyches.' Mr O'Brien adds that in the few cases in which complications occur, the lack of medical care in, say, Africa – which would normally save the day here – often results in poor outcomes. I might add that the risk of dying in childbirth in the UK is ten per 100,000 compared with 790 per 100,000 in Sierra Leone.

many parts of the world where women unhappily have no alternative and where one mother in 20 can expect to lose her baby and one in 300 her own life. Before we take off for the moon and the stars, let us try to remember that the most important thing about birthdays is that both the mother and the child should survive.

Journal of Perinatology, Summer 1987

Milk Banks: In the Light of History

Thirty years ago, the milk came frozen on the night train from Cardiff, and was collected by nurses in the bleak and chilly dawn on Paddington Station. Back at the ranch, from Llandough to Llanedeyrn, the mothers took their milk to St David's at a penny an ounce to feed premature babies in London and make ends meet at home. Quality checks were unheard of, but if it passed the sharp eyes and nose of the bank sister, with a fearsome reputation for sniffing out the merest drop of added water, it was widely regarded the ideal food for premature babies.

The results were not good and said more for the fortitude of babies than the milk squirted into their mouths through Belcroy feeders. But with a perinatal mortality of 35 per cent and wages under the breadline, a milk bank only had beggars, not choosers.

Inevitably, measurements increasingly took the guess-work out of what was needed and what was given. Slowly but surely, the feeding of low birth weight babies became as much a science as an art. EBM and milk banks gave way to special formulae with the sterility of an autoclave, the purity of holy water, and the nutritional bricks and mortar to match placentas which could treble a baby's size in the last three months in utero. The babies thrived and this part of the story is an outstanding success.

The problem with human milk is knowing exactly what it contains. A sniff, however highly developed, is obviously not enough and disturbing facts emerged when technology probed its secrets. It is clearly no longer acceptable to feed untreated samples of unknown composition from unknown donors to our most fragile citizens. Responsible milk banks have been quick to respond with increasingly complicated and costly manipulations to make their milks safer and more wholesome. There are limits, however, and when it comes to monthly checks on the personal life-styles and HIV status of donors, as now recommended by the Chief Medical Officer, these have surely been reached if not breached.

Less responsible banks, which outnumber the scrupulous, prefer to believe no problems exist. To look for contamination is to find it, while sterilising takes away the 'goodness' and adding nutrients is seen to defeat the object of the exercise. There is a certain bliss in ignorance but, to our cost, we have now reached an era when it is not enough to kill all known germs. We must also kill the unknown ones.

It is important to see the changes which have taken place in the light of history, if only to make sure that we do not turn back the clock and repeat the mistakes of the past. For many years, human milk has been the gold standard on which the best substitutes were modelled. But low birth weight infants indisputably have gold standards all of their own. Paradoxically, if we are to feed them human milk, it must now be strictly modelled on the best substitutes.

Midwife, Health Visitor & Community Nurse, July 1988

'Cookie' – a Mistaken Case of Child Abuse

Cookie was not her real name. I have changed it to conceal her identity, but it was equally bizarre and just the sort of name to put you on your guard. My suspicions only deepened as the mother's story unfolded.

To begin with, she came without a doctor's letter. She had somehow managed to bypass the system and get an appointment without a GP referral. Her GP was useless, she explained, leaving a name which, as it turned out, was not to be found in the medical or the telephone directory.

It then transpired that Cookie, who was two years old, had already been to three different hospitals in three weeks for the same complaint – a sore bottom. All three hospitals were just as useless, she said. They gave Cookie medicines for constipation when it was obvious she was constipated only because she was in severe pain. With each treatment the bottom had got worse and matters were now desperate.

The mother was young, unmarried, unsupported and unemployed. She had parted company with her family who were in Scotland where Cookie had been born. She neither knew nor cared about the father's whereabouts. Although she had lived in London for a year, she did not have a social worker or a health visitor. In Scotland, however, she had had to take Cookie at least half a dozen times to local Accident and Emergency departments for diarrhoea and vomiting.

The sore bottom had started three weeks earlier. The GP gave her Mil-Par. Hospital A gave her Canesten cream, Hospital B lactulose syrup and Hospital C glycerine suppositories. By this time, the stools were bloodstained and watery and she was in terrible pain.

On examination, Cookie was very frightened, tearful

and upset, as was only to be expected. She clung to her mother for all she was worth, and refused to be weighed, undressed or examined. She looked well-cared-for but both she and her mother were distressed and distraught.

It was not easy to get a good look at the perineum and what I could see was not reassuring. The anus was tightly closed – an impregnable barrier defying anyone who might try to insert another suppository. The perianal skin was intensely sore and oedematous, with redness spreading up to the vulva. All round the anus were small, bleeding islands of denuded skin and heaped-up bluish areas of what looked like bruising. The hymen was intact and there was no discharge.

Cookie's mother fiercely denied any possibility that she might have been injured. She had no contact with her father or any other relatives and was never out of her mother's sight. And, yet, the picture was striking. Whole families have been disrupted by those who, rightly or wrongly, see anal abuse on lesser grounds by far. To tear this sad, insecure, clinging couple asunder was not a pleasant thought.

To give me a chance to find out what had already been done, I told the mother I would do some tests and asked her to return later that day. Meanwhile, I gave her a soothing protective cream to apply.

I have never subscribed to the multi-disciplinary sledge-hammer approach, with its beloved case conferences and diagnosis by committee. My rapport with the Social Services is as cool as a Siberian winter. To make an accurate diagnosis, it is important to perform the right investigations and not confuse the issue with misleading information. I therefore like to plan the necessary enquiries myself, as in any other complaint, and as most people expect on seeking medical attention.

The first two lines of inquiry drew a blank. The GP was not listed in any directory, although it transpired later that he did in fact exist. Hospital A had the prevalent NHS organisation which ensured that I received a reply three months after the trouble was over.

My third telephone call misfired badly, as I feared it might. I was keen to involve the health visitor and called the Director of Community Nursing, explaining that the child was not in danger. 'I hear what you are saying,' she said ominously. By the time Cookie and her mother got home, two plain-clothes police officers were waiting at the door. In fact, no health visitor ever came, thus denying me her valuable collaboration, and the mother and child her help and support at a time of great stress. I doubt if I would take such a risk again. If there is a moral to this sorry tale, it is surely that no nurse manager should ever take the law into her own hands when specifically asked to observe confidentiality.

The next call, to the paediatrician at Hospital B, struck gold. She also worked at Hospital C and was able to read the case-notes from both hospitals over to me only 30 minutes later. Two vital pieces of information emerged. Firstly, that the condition had steadily become worse over the three weeks. And secondly, that she had once seen a similarly dramatic perianal rash caused by a streptococcal infection. It is not well-known, nor is it described in books and articles on sexual abuse, although the two conditions look very similar. A streptococcal infection of the skin responds to penicillin and is better in a matter of days.

In contrast to the Social Services, my contact with police officers has always been cordial. A long talk with a sympathetic inspector defused the situation as far as the police were concerned. My last call to the community paediatrician on the Child Protection Team also helped to put off any action for the time being.

Cookie's mother returned that evening in a high dudgeon, as she had every right to be. After calming her down, the important task was to take a swab and get Cookie started on a course of oral penicillin while waiting for the result. The swab grew *haemolytic streptococcus*, sensitive to penicillin. Three days later, the rash had gone and Cookie was back to normal. The Social Services held their case conference as planned, of course. A dozen people sat round a table for an hour talking about a child of whom they knew nothing and a rash which was no longer there.

They say that truth is stranger than fiction. Roald Dahl, that master of *Tales of the Unexpected*, would have relished the sting in this tail.

Midwife, Health Visitor & Community Nurse, June 1991

Cot Deaths

Cot death is the sudden and unexpected death of a baby for no apparent reason. There were 1,047 such deaths of young babies in England and Wales last year. Unfortunately, efforts to reduce this tragic loss of life have been hindered by the failure to find the basic cause, despite enormous scientific efforts.

The bitterness of bereaved parents who believe they could have done something to lessen the risk is understandable and, at long last, some recommendations have received official blessing and will be adopted nationwide.

Sleeping Position

Research into 241 cot deaths carried out in 1983 revealed that 94% of the babies were found lying face down. Mounting evidence has pointed to the higher risk of the face-down position which should have been strongly discouraged over 10 years ago. While the fear of actual choking or suffocation is probably exaggerated, both the face-down and face-up positions carry an element of risk. A young baby who vomits a feed while lying on his back is not sufficiently advanced to turn his head to one side. Similarly, a large amount of vomit on a cot sheet in front of the face may turn it into an airtight seal. Therefore, the safest position is on one side with a rolled towel or baby wedge behind the back to keep the baby in this position.

Sleeping on an Incline

The controversy over sleeping positions has focused far too long on one horizontal position versus another and missed the most important point of all, which is to raise the head of the cot. Laying the baby at an incline of 15 – 20 degrees substantially reduces heartburn and eases pressure on the diaphragm.

Babies in the first six months consume large liquid feeds and go to sleep almost immediately afterwards. Six ounces of milk inside a baby of 10 lbs is equal to five pints in an adult, and few adults stretch out flat straight after a heavy meal and certainly not face down.

The head of a cot can easily be propped on books, blocks, bricks or a polystyrene wedge, however, it would be much more effective if cots were made with the correct incline built in.

Location of Cot

No parents can be reasonably expected to keep watch over a baby every minute of the day and night. This level of observation is neither necessary nor practical and most parents soon come to a sensible compromise. In the first six months, the best place for the cot at night is in the parents' room where the chances of hearing a baby in difficulty are better than in a separate nursery.

Breastfeeding

I do not believe that one kind of milk is any more to blame than another, and no mother should be made to feel guilty about the method of feeding she chooses. Breastfeeding does have some hidden advantages, however. The intervals between feeds are shorter and the babies are more wakeful and generally spend less time asleep. Night feeds go on longer and mothers are more likely to keep the cot nearby for convenience, so the total time actually spent handling a breastfed baby is probably greater than for a bottle-fed baby.

There will always be mothers who are unable to breastfeed and it must be stressed that any advantages with regard to cot death are slight. Laying the baby to sleep on his side, with his head raised, and putting the cot in the same room as the parents are far more important.

Monitoring

Currently, instruments for monitoring baby range from simple home baby-listening devices, to more elaborate breathing monitors, heart recorders and oxygen meters, for which proper supervision is essential. What is needed is an instrument which not only alerts parents that the baby is unwell but also stimulates respiration. There are monitors on loan to selected families, funded by donations to hospitals and charities. If you are anxious and would like a home monitor, it should be provided with careful instructions for action to take in a genuine emergency. Parents who are worried enough to ask for a monitor also need professional help for which there is no simple mechanical substitute.

Maternity and Mothercraft, February 1992

Citation
Dr Richard John Cremer

The 1950s were exciting times in paediatrics. Special care baby units were springing up beside maternity departments across the country, and a new breed of paediatricians, previously trained in children's hospitals, where babies were never born, began to take an interest in the care of the newborn.

Richard Cremer belonged to this generation when, as paediatric registrar at the Rochford General Hospital from 1956 – 1958, he was the moving force behind a remarkable series of observations which were to enlighten newborn care. Then untrammelled by purchasers and bureaucracy, he and two colleagues opened a new chapter in newborn care and entered Rochford into medical history. That he eventually chose general practice was a loss to paediatrics, albeit to the immense gain of many fortunate families in Wallington.

Rochford is not particularly noted for its climate or thought to be a corner of Essex forever bathed in sunshine. Luckily, in the summer of 1956, the sun shone long enough for three puzzling events to occur. First, a previously jaundiced baby turned pale except for a patch of yellow where the skin had been covered by a cot sheet. Then, a blood specimen which had been left on a window sill registered an unexpectedly low and clearly wrong plasma bilirubin. Lastly, having spent the best part of a fine sunny afternoon on an exchange transfusion, Richard was chagrined to hear that the bilirubin was lower in the blood samples before he started than after he finished.

As the saying goes:

Large streams from little fountains flow,
Tall oaks from little acorns grow

Richard and his chastened colleagues in the laboratory set about explaining the seemingly inexplicable. Soon, as jaundiced babies basked in the sunshine, the window sill in the biochemistry laboratory sported an array of blood samples which changed colour like traffic lights.

The results of months of frantic activity appeared in *The Lancet* on 24th May 1958. Bilirubin is broken down by sunlight or artificial light, and exposing the skin of jaundiced babies will lower their serum bilirubin levels. Looking back on it now, this modest report was remarkably complete in itself.

It took time before the findings were confirmed and accepted, but phototherapy came to revolutionise the management of hyperbilirubinaemia in babies to this day. Much high-powered research since then has added little of practical importance except to submerge its origins. Almost 40 years ago, Richard Cremer pressed a switch which turned on lights in special care baby units throughout the world. Few discoveries in medicine can claim to have burned longer or brighter.

July 1996

Miss Roisin McAuley
BBC Radio 4
Broadcasting House
London W1A 1AA   14 September 2001

Dear Miss McAuley,

I happened to hear your programme on September 12 about the influx of Ugandan Asians in 1972. You may be interested in a small aspect which is unlikely to have received any attention all these years.

Now retired, I was a consultant paediatrician at Charing Cross Hospital at the time. We had only just brought the devastating effects of congenital rubella – i.e., deafness, heart defects and mental retardation in the babies of mothers who had German measles in early pregnancy – under control by a vigorous national programme of vaccination for 10 years or more.

I was horrified by the idea of thousands of unprotected young Asian women and girls coming into Britain. The then DHSS policy was not to vaccinate boys, and rubella was therefore still rife in the general population. Girls coming from Uganda would have had little chance to acquire natural immunity and would probably not have been vaccinated there. Many would undoubtedly go on to have babies in the next few years and a proportion would inevitably pick up German measles in early pregnancy.

I at once wrote to the Department of Health to express my worst fears and to suggest that all unvaccinated girls and women of child-bearing age should be offered rubella vaccination *on entry*. Sometime later I received the usual short, unhelpful reply which was basically to the effect that the DHSS had no intention of doing anything in the matter.

Not surprisingly, the annual prevalence of congenital rubella, having fallen to single figures, once again rose to double figures over the next few years.

All this is ancient history now, but your programme reminded me of something I feel particularly bitter about. The total number of affected babies is numerically small and merely a blip on the charts of 25 – 30 years ago, but the cost of human tragedy in each family must have been immense.

Yours sincerely,
Herbert Barrie MD, FRCP, FRCPCH
Consultant Paediatrician

Commentary

When I took up my appointment at Charing Cross Hospital in 1966, the so-called 'Prem Unit' was a small, airless prefab which even the occupants of Calcutta's Black Hole would have regarded less congenial.

Five years later, we had piped oxygen and air, proper ventilation and air conditioning and our own ambulance, a sort of SCBU[46] on wheels, for collecting babies from far and wide. With no maternity beds at Fulham, all referrals came from elsewhere. The NHS contribution for all this was minimal and even the piped oxygen was a gift from British Oxygen in a rare show of philanthropy.

In 1972, I approached Mothercare to sponsor a leaflet the team could leave parents before we took the baby away. This, plus a rather foggy Polaroid snapshot, were two small tokens to show that we cared. Elegantly printed on glossy paper, it was probably the first of its kind.

The babies pictured in that leaflet are now over 30 years old and the students who posed as their parents must be nearing retirement. Your own current SHOs and registrars had not been born. Consent was not a major factor in 1972 and our leaflet was more intended to carry information and hope.

Shortly after starting to hand it out, I received a curt note from the House Governor forbidding us to use it and to destroy the 1,000 or so copies Mothercare had generously printed. (He was actually a very decent person and very able administrator, so this unexpected row over nothing was totally out of character.) Apparently, he took exception to the following sentence: 'Because the care of the babies is the

---

46. Special care baby unit (now known as neonatal unit).

most important consideration, it is not always possible to keep you fully informed of all that is being done.'

I naturally refused and the dispute rapidly blew up into a major war. Battle lines were drawn, knives sharpened, axes ground and unlikely alliances forged. Sworn enemies for years suddenly became bedfellows.

As if the affair had not already spiralled out of control enough, the House Governor saw fit to involve the MDU[47] of which I was a member but he, of course, was not. The Secretary of the MDU happily obliged with the extraordinary opinion that the leaflet was dangerous without thinking to ascertain the author.

I was outraged, as were several colleagues who threatened to resign from the MDU and join the MPS.[48] I sent a strong protest to the MDU President, whose grandchild I happened to be looking after at the time.

Apart from the storm now raging at the MDU, the battle at Charing Cross was about to culminate in an extraordinary meeting of the full Medical Committee of all 80 or so consultants. Here the House Governor could expect to be heavily outnumbered, especially by those who felt their freedom of expression in *The Lancet* or *Spectator* was under threat. There were dark mutterings of a vote of censure – the first in the 150-year history of the hospital.

Two days before the fateful meeting, the House Governor asked to see me and made the penitent journey from The Strand to Fulham. He apologised and offered to make amends which I was happy to accept. The nearby occupational therapy hut was about to be vacated and was just what I needed for a neonatal research laboratory. We

---

47. Medical Defence Union.

48. Medical Protection Society. The MDU and MPS are medical indemnity organisations.

shook hands on the deal, the meeting was called off and peace was restored.

It was a major territorial gain. Six months later, with a large grant from Cow & Gate, the laboratory was up and running with a research fellow, technician and state-of-the-art analysers which enabled us to check our own blood gases, electrolytes and bilirubins on microsamples as often and whenever we liked. This may now be normal NICU[49] practice, but 30 years ago it was almost unique. We never made any earth-shattering discoveries but a lot of lives were saved in the process.

Newsletter of the Royal College of Paediatrics and Child Health, February 2003

---

49. Neonatal intensive care unit, i.e., neonatal unit.

Letter to Bertie Sugarman, a Friend

Dear Bertie,

Why I left Victim Support

This is how it happened.

A Korean student was mugged on Kingston Hill so we enlisted the help of a volunteer with the unlikely name of Sam Sung. His English was unfortunately limited to a single phrase: 'Bless my soul', which could be his national anthem for all I know. Although his native language may have been beyond reproach, it was very difficult if not impossible to tell him what to say to victims or report back what they told him.

We decided to give the student a personal alarm. This is a gadget the size of a packet of cigarettes which emits a deafening screech by pulling out a small pin on a length of cord. You tie the other end of the cord to yourself and, when threatened, pull the pin out and fling the box as far as you can. The ear-splitting din goes on until the battery gives out or the pin is put back. Since pin and box are now meters apart, this is not a ready option for the average head-shaved yob.

Sam was given the task of presenting the student with the alarm and my role was to keep an eye on him. By means of expansive sign language and much blessings of soul or Seoul, we arranged to meet separately at the address in Norbiton. Unfortunately, he arrived at the venue early, knocked on the door and rang the bell. Receiving no answer, he then made the fateful blunder that was to precipitate my departure from Victim Support and the management committee. At this point, I must correct your misapprehensions concerning my constabulary duties. The two are totally separate and leaving VS (Victim Support) has actually enabled me to work more shifts at VN ('Victor' New Malden Police).

Back at the ranch in Norbiton, as they say, Sam decided to put the alarm through the letter box. As it was too thick to go through in its cardboard box and even in just its protective bubble wrapping, he carefully removed all wrapping. Then, hanging on to the end of the string for dear life, he fed the alarm through the letter box to embark on its first precarious descent to the floor.

Unfortunately the height of the letter box was greater than the length of the string, leaving the alarm to dangle precariously some ten inches off the floor by its pin. He therefore decided to haul it back, which he did not without justifiable trepidation. He retrieved it as far as the letter-box but then it got stuck, the box, to his chagrin, having been fitted with bristle brushes designed to let articles in but not out. He debated momentarily whether to give the cord a sharp tug but thought better of it. He looked round hopefully, as he had heard somewhere in Korea that small English boys always carry bits of string in their pockets. There were no small boys in sight, but looking down at his feet he had a sudden inspiration. He undid one shoelace and knotted one end gingerly to the cord from the alarm.

The alarm began its second precarious descent, this time with Sam hanging on to the end of the shoelace for dear life, and it landed safely on the floor without so much as a plop. He let go of the shoelace, which disappeared between the bristles just as I arrived and witnessed at first hand the catastrophic events that were to follow.

Suddenly all hell broke loose. A dog, apparently asleep

hitherto, woke with a start and hurled itself at the unfamiliar object with cataclysmic ferocity, seized it in slavering jaws and shook it with murderous violence. Not built to withstand this kind of onslaught, the pin was dislodged and the alarm went off with a screech audible to a distance of twenty houses in all directions. The dog bounded upstairs in terror and stood howling by the furthermost window like a coyote in the Nebraska desert. Doors and windows began to open up and down the street like dominoes, heads popped out of skylights in roof conversions and right-angled necks craned from boxy first-floor extensions stuck on the side.

In no time there were three police cars, and one ambulance summoned by a neighbour who in the heat of the moment forgot to say the patient was a dog. All had flashing beacons and blaring sirens and the pandemonium defies description. The police immediately set about breaking down the door, which of course did not belong to the student but her landlady. Two burly coppers stuck their fingers in their ears and jumped up and down on the alarm in a vain attempt to stop the screeching which I eventually stopped by putting the pin back. Sam fled the scene and, impeded by the absence of a lace on one shoe, could be seen disappearing in the far distance in a curious locomotion best described as a hop, skip and jump. One or two bystanders thought they heard him gasp, 'Bless my soul' under his breath as he hopped along.

Peace eventually returned to the previously quiet Norbiton street, but the thought of something similar again was more than I could face. Now you know why I left Victim Support.

With best wishes,
Herbert
January 2004

Letter to Dr David Curnock,
Emeritus Consultant Paediatrician,
Nottingham City Hospital

Dear David,

Thank you very much for your letter. I am sure all the alumni at the recent reunion are distinguished in their way but it can claim only two saints – you and Anne for your tireless work in Tanzania and Bulgaria. The two isolated and disadvantaged communities are a far cry from Nottingham, and your selfless input must make a huge difference. On top of your efforts, you have probably had to familiarise yourselves with the local languages, cultures, customs and diseases. Your elegant Power Point presentation tables show the steady impact of your visits.

I hope this belated letter reaches you before your next return to Stara Zagora, if not to a waiting red carpet then to the many uplifted hearts of grateful children and parents. Like you, I have been catching up on my correspondence but with no truthful excuse except idleness and the slow pace of old age. I used to be able to dictate dozens of letters to wonderful secretaries and dash off articles and reports on my old Amstrad when I got home, but that was years ago. I now use a PC and everything takes ten times as long.

I too of course cherish countless memories of you, but two stand out in particular. The first was your scholarly and tempestuous introduction to a study on head circumferences: *Now does my project gather to a head*, which must have had Shakespeare's bones rolling in the aisles of Stratford's Holy Trinity.

And on the subject of keeping one's head, the other

was your consummate calm when all around was panic. A toddler in a deep coma in our ITU[50] at Charing Cross had suddenly regained consciousness, torn the drip from her arm, knocked the stand over and sent a tray of instruments flying. You telephoned me: it was 2am and all I could hear was the sound of breaking glass, screams and shouts and general pandemonium in the background. Your unforgettable response was: 'I think there has been a development.'

Of my wonderful secretaries, I guess Jill Wilson was working in the department in your time at Charing Cross. I am in regular touch with her, and Jane, her successor. Jill and Jane were magnificent. I also get yearly cards from Hazel Maycock, my brilliant SCBU[51] nursing sister, and even some of the children and prems[52] we looked after. Did you know one is an Oscar-awarded film star?

I am in the process of shredding a lot of old documents and came across a SCBU report for the momentous year of 1977 when we had the good fortune to have an exceptional registrar and a PMR[53] of just 16.4 per 1,000. I can't think why I have kept these papers all these years. It is all ancient history of no interest to anybody.

Looking back, one of the changes of which I am especially proud are the many Charing Cross graduates who specialised in paediatrics after my arrival, when to the best of my knowledge there were only two in the ten years before. I cannot really take any credit for this other than to persuade the powers-that-be that the paediatric department was no place for pre-registration house officers and that all

---

50. Intensive care unit.

51. Special care baby unit (now known as neonatal unit).

52. Premature babies.

53. Perinatal mortality rate.

our house officers should be SHOs.[54] I am sure this was the single most important turning point in producing so many paediatricians and DCH[55]–holding GPs.

I wish you all success and good health,

Herbert

January 2012

---

54. Senior house officers.
55. Diploma in child health.

Letter to Chris Prance, a Friend

Dear Chris,

Thank you for your letter awash with spicy news and youthful adventure.

I wish I could draw like you and cram as much as you do into each day. Star-gazing, cloud-watching, clock-ticking, brisk walks (many a time behind a loaded wheelbarrow), games with the grandchildren, lead strummer at thronged ukulele gigs, Gurkha gourmets, enjoying the ripples of the waves in golden sands of time and hunting your family name to its piratical roots when you have a spare moment. Afflicted as I am with insomnia, I envy anybody who can drop off to sleep like a baby in the middle of the day and ride the twice-yearly changing of the clocks like a surfer in St Ives.

As you say, one thousand guineas must have been an astronomical sum in those days. Most of it probably went on paying Blackbeard's band of fellow cut-throats which is why none of it is left. However, what came of his notorious treasure? *Captain, art thou sleeping there below?* Somewhere among the barnacles at the bottom of the sea lies a crock of gold. If you can find the exact position where the buccaneer went down and give a passing thought to hire a schooner in search, it would make your GP's parting shot a remarkable stroke of intuitive perspicacity. Who needs Doc Martin?

For my part, I get out of breath just getting up in the morning. Everything is an effort apart from sitting down. Admittedly I am not down to a stick or Zimmer frame yet and can still go up and down stairs, but I do seem to spend most of my time doing nothing. I would like to be a bit slimmer but spend so little energy now it would take a spell in Kingston Hospital on 'nil by mouth' or Wormwood Scrubs to lose a few pounds. Incidentally, have you noticed how fit and well the migrants look in spite of whatever they are running away from?

My birthday passed uneventfully after having let it be known that I did not want any fuss. Michael insisted on taking me out for lunch last week to Warren House to meet somebody[56] I have not seen for 60 years – a one-time GP turned writer, speaker, entertainer, broadcaster and author of medical programmes. In other words, a sort of Jonathan Miller without the opera and the hubris. Warren House, if you have never been inside, is a Victorian mini-palace in Warren Road with sumptuous grounds, interior, furniture and works of art. All the more surprising to have a bunch of jeaned, tattooed, hirsute, local hoi polloi at the next table. But then, every priceless Persian rug has its flaw.

There is only a week in age between us but it might as well be 20 years. You have the edge by a very wide margin in everything, with the possible exception of medical science. Even here we are on a par, since I cannot even peer into my own ears to see if they are blocked with wax. By no conceivable contrivance with mirrors can I get a close-up of an unbearably itchy spot on my back. I cannot even reach it for a good scratch. The laws of physics dictate that reflected images are twice the distance of the subject in front. I could ask Dinah but she refuses to wear varifocals and always has the wrong glasses on, and in any case cannot tell a pimple from a pox. But give her a culture plate covered in deadly bacteria and she is in seventh heaven.

The GPs in my NHS practice are nice ladies, not that

---

56. Dr Michael O'Donnell.

I mind. I have a friend who loves his lady GP dearly for anything above the waist but consults Michael for anything below, which of course causes endless confusion. It won't be long before male GPs are officially declared a threatened species like pandas and beluga whales.

I manage my own complaints most of the time and rarely visit my NHS GPs (Michael's old practice in Kingston) except to add to their 'brownie points' for occasional blood tests or weight checks. Repeat prescriptions are taken care of electronically by a local pharmacy which I enter and leave steadily by sexless automatic sliding doors.

I think I can explain your friend's unfortunate disability – what is known as 'spastic diplegia' and commonly the result of acute birth asphyxia. Much of my paediatric career was devoted to spreading the gospel of effective neonatal resuscitation to prevent this very disaster.

About the lucky goldfish in your devoted care. The frost forecast by the early arrival of a wild duck from Siberia may never happen but it is right to be prepared. Being poikilothermic, fish lower their body temperature in cold weather and can withstand cold but can run out of oxygen when a pond freezes right over, and die of fright if you crack the ice with a hammer. The best precaution is to keep a small ring of water from freezing with an immersion heater. Designed for the purpose, it is perfectly safe, does not harm the fish and uses very little electricity. Any decent aquatic shop should stock it or you could order one online.

At this moment in time, to use a jobsworth's vernacular, I am sitting in the kitchen at 9pm with my laptop and the front of the house shrouded in darkness. It is Halloween and the little children have been and gone. Naturally, as a paediatrician, I approve of small children who get plied generously with fun-sized chocolate bars under the watchful eyes of their mothers. After 9pm, however, our road is plagued with large louts who frighten old ladies out of their skins and think nothing of breaking a window or two. My tactic in recent years has been to go out for the evening or re-enact the strict blackout in the Blitz.

With best wishes,

Herbert

January 2012

Letter to Wilfried Kratz, a Friend

Dear Wilfried,

Tempora mutantur!

How times fly, especially if a clock falls off the mantelpiece or the *leichtlebige Frau's* tattooed eagle withers to a sparrow. I am happy to report that I have no tattoos and nothing quite so depressing has happened to me apart from feeling ten years older in ten days.

Recent events have reminded me of four short stories I wrote over 50 years ago. One was on the decline of baby clinics and their conversion to elderly care centres – with the same old rubber sheets, free vitamins, dominoes for bricks, wheelchairs in the old pram shelters and evening son-and-daughter craft classes after Granny and Grandad had gone to bed.

Another which was remarkably prescient was about a 90-year-old man who ran away from an old people's home. That particular little tale, which was entirely fictitious, prompted a tearful reader in Australia to write to me offering to look after him for the rest of his life. Today's *Telegraph* has a picture of a 90-year-old D-Day veteran surrounded by 2,500 greetings cards after running away from his old-age home to join the anniversary parade in Normandy. Despite all the bad press about abuse in many elderly care homes recently, they made a huge fuss of him when he was brought back unrepentant and treated him like a hero all over again.

Even in my imagination, I could not have predicted I would wake up one morning two weeks ago with a pain in my left knee which rapidly went from bad to worse and from worse to intolerable. I soon ran out of my gamut of ineffective self-medications and called in Michael – my GP adviser when I run out of ideas and need somebody more up to date and 'with it'.

By Wednesday I was reduced to crawling round on two hands and one good knee, and so Michael admitted me to Kingston Hospital for intravenous pain relief.

> *Some doctor full of phrase and fame,*
> *To shake his sapient head and give*
> *The ill he cannot cure a name.*

Strictly speaking, this was not quite true since I had already guessed it might be a form of gout, but Michael called it pseudogout and said I might possibly have a septic arthritis, so I finished up being treated for both at the same time for the next five days. The intravenous pain relief for which I had yearned proved rather disappointing, with the result that I went right off my food and with six-hourly blood checks managed to lose half a stone in weight. This, at least, was one beneficial outcome of a most disagreeable episode and I am now 5kg lighter. In the absence of any evidence of sepsis, the final diagnosis was calcium pyrophosphate dihydrate disease, otherwise known as pseudogout, which when I was a student was simply called gout.

Something of an unkind joke ascribed to an overindulgence of vintage port at the time, gout was treated with applications of boiled rosemary leaves by buxom potato-faced wenches in lacy mob caps summoned from the bowels of the hospital kitchen who would recycle the leaves in the patients' next lamb *Eintopfgerichte*. The current position is that I can walk short distances, go up and down stairs, drive my Jaguar and sleep reasonably well, but standing on a straight left leg is uncomfortable. House chores and gardening are out and if I have to stand, I stand on one leg like a stork, and hope not to fall over.

With best wishes,

Herbert

June 2014

Letter to Chris Prance, a Friend

Dear Chris,

Thank goodness Christmas is over. Perish the thought of the crashing crescendo all over again next December.

The unashamed commercialism spreads like the 'flu and gets worse every year to the point of people killing each other over a toaster at pre-Christmas sales. I get deluged with begging letters from charities I already support generously, bulging with tacky labels, gift tags, cardboard wine-glass mats and pens that don't work. It makes one wonder whether they all subsidise the same fundraising company with my money.

On TV, all 86 channels churn out schmaltzy Santa films with six inches of deep snow which never thaws, never freezes and never buries sheep in the hills or causes mayhem on roads, railways or at airports. They also wheel out an endless supply of repeats even older than Methuselah like *Goodbye, Mr. Chips.*

I have a special aversion for advertisements which take up not just a whole page but two or even four. My *Daily Telegraph* gets fatter and fatter and now barely squeezes through the letter box. This morning's was wrapped in a four-page spread to go to Ireland, for goodness' sake. And I am not remotely tempted by the anorexic model on a swing to invest in a pea-sized bottle of Chanel No. 5.

I also wonder how much longer I can hump the lights, wreath, baubles and manger down, and then back up, my loft ladder without risk to life and limb. I get short of breath poaching enough electric adaptor plugs from around the house simply to get the bulbs to work. The last straw is always having to drag the perishing tree into the garden in a trail of pine needles. A few days ago Michael asked me about writing my own obituary, mainly to save him the trouble later. Michael has the curious but well-intentioned belief that I am not likely to write anything derogatory about myself. Strangely enough, never having attempted any obituaries, this has really thrown me. I am lost for words, looking at blank sheets of paper and a wastepaper bin brim-full with scrunched-up balls of paper. I really wouldn't know where to start.[57]

I did in fact do something today I always said I would never contemplate, namely climb onto my garage roof and clear the gutter of leaves, bird droppings and other occluding detritus. With dirty rainwater spilling onto the cars below and the offending blockage not strictly within the remit of the window cleaner or gardeners, I had little choice but to do the perishing job myself. I am glad to report I got onto the roof and back without injury to life or limb and, as George Bush famously said, 'Mission accomplished.' Nevertheless, I urge you not to try this at home.

In case you are wondering whether my many messages, including your own, for a 'merry, happy and joyful Christmas' bore fruit, we spent 21st December in what used to be The Albert Arms and is now The Albert to celebrate Robert's[58] 18th birthday. This hostelry has evidently gone upmarket since my last visit. It has been extensively refurbished inside and out and acquired a useful car park. Small children and dogs are welcome, and more burgers with chips are consumed than alcohol.

Our entire family of thirteen (two pairs of grandparents, two pairs of parents and assorted grandsons) reconvened at

---

57. Alas, Dad never did write his obituary – not one word!
58. Robert, his grandson.

Michael's brother-in-law's[59] house on Christmas Day where a good time was had by all. His wife, Rebecca, is delightful; she comes from Ohio and is like a breath of fresh air. I 'fiddled' my repertoire of carols and Caroline blew hers on the clarinet, but not in unison owing to insurmountable vagaries of pitch between the two instruments. Rebecca played Pachelbel's *canon* on the piano and I accompanied her on violin. I am reliably informed by the local Pest Control that all mice have disappeared within a mile radius.

Which brings me to the fine job you did playing your ukulele for the worthies of Ilfracombe. I am not sure hymn sheets would have helped, bearing in mind that half the souls generously bussed in by Age Concern would have been hard of hearing or had poor vision. Those unable to hear would have joined in with wrong words whilst those unable to see would have had to *la-la-la* all the verses.

I sympathise with your unfortunate experience with the Lidl lobster. I venture into our Lidl sometimes as it is the only remaining local store with an in-house bakery. Although I pride myself on being reasonably democratic, broad-minded, reasonably tolerant and completely non-racist, the Lidl experience is like visiting the refugee camps outside Calais or the parts of the world from whence they came. In the spirit of *Deutschland über Alles,* I hope you have noticed that all prices are displayed *above* the items on the shelves instead of below as in all other stores.

Here's wishing you a Happy New Year, good health, happiness and prosperity,

Herbert

January 2015

---

59. Nimesh Patel.

Letter to Chris Prance, a Friend

Dear Chris,

As a *Telegraph* cryptic crossword addict, I am often intrigued by the hidden meaning of your email titles, never more so than by your last, 'Steady as she goes.' You have written that it is what your kindly GP said to you on the way out of his consulting room, which makes me conjecture all the more as to its true meaning. Several possibilities spring to mind:

1. It is a 'goodbye' vernacular peculiar to the West Country, like 'ta-ra' in Liverpool or 'take care' in downtown Miami.
2. You have a Zimmer frame named after one of your Bradford ponies.
3. Your GP's surgery is offshore and only reached by sailing boat.
4. Your GP never looked up from his computer throughout the consultation and failed to notice she was a he.
5. He has been reading Shakespeare again.
6. Should have gone to SpecSavers.

Sorry to hear about all that scaffolding. In my experience, scaffolders can usually be distinguished by their corpulence, lurid tattoos, shaved heads and lewd whistles to passing females. They relish in what is at best a noisy occupation and make the most of it by banging the rusty rods about, shouting at each other and playing radios. The industry is sustained by the length of time the structure is on hire, so it stays in place for months if not years and certainly long after it is no longer required. It has to be said that scaffolding is no worse an eyesore than many critically lauded examples of modern sculpture. If and when it is eventually dismantled – an even noisier affair than putting it up – you can expect to endure a comparable example of modern music.

With best wishes,

Herbert

September 2015

Letter to Chris Prance, a Friend

Dear Chris,

I gave away two electric coffee grinders a few years ago and I am now seriously tempted to buy a new one. It would have to be electric – life is enough of a grind without winding myself up in my search for the perfect cuppa. I have been through various brands of coffee at various strengths and served in cafetières, filters and espresso pots without matching the marvellous brew in any humble run-of-the mill (if you will pardon the pun) German or Italian café. Dishing it up in enormous one-pint plastic mugs, regarded the height of fashion here, simply makes the experience as disgusting as the dishwatery contents.

Our local Waitrose offers free coffee (in a large, flimsy, disposable plastic mug of course) to anybody who wants it. Needless to say, there is always a queue of people who can never resist a freebie, even a tiny cube of stale Cheddar on a stick on the cheese counter. Some come in for the coffee without buying anything. The rest just get in the way, clutching their steaming carton in one hand and a mobile phone clapped to an ear in the other. I have not tried the coffee, but it smells revolting enough to want to retreat smartly to a part of the shop where you can't smell it.

The range of brands and blends on the shelves is intentionally bewildering. Colombian, Brazilian, Costa Rican, Ecuadorian, Italian, Ethiopian, Kenyan etc. – you name it, it is all there except Taiwanese. If and when you find the perfect blend, please let me know.

Mr Cor Blimey is a roofer who has served us well for 25 years. Cor Blimey is not his real name but it's not a tile's throw from it. He has seen us through wet events of one sort or another over the years and on our commendation has looked after half the neighbourhood's roofs. So when our garage roof began to drip rainwater on the cars, I naturally turned to him to fix the problem. It is a sad fact of life that A&E departments up and down the country are swamped by old men falling off ladders. Small wonder then that the NHS is on its knees! I stopped clambering up ladders years ago. No good telling me 'steady as she goes' when I'm up a ten-foot ladder. Consequently I did not perform a naked-eye inspection of the problem myself. Flat roofs are known to spell trouble, and I willingly went along with the advice to re-cover it with a new layer of roofing-felt laid on top of the old one.

A month or two of dry weather went by. Then, after a heavy downpour (as forecast by Miss Welby in a stunning, blue sleeveless dress), guess what? Drip, drip, drip. Mr C returned and enlarged the outflow hole at the end of the gully. More fine weather, another shower and... drip, drip, drip. *Cor Blimey...!* At his third visit, Mr C wedged a stone under the bottom of the downpipe from the gully. Another dry spell, shower, drip, drip, drip. My medical instincts at this stage prompted me to seek a second opinion, aka Checkatrade.com, resulting, to cut a long story short, in a prompt diagnosis and successful treatment. The new man obligingly photographed the problem for me on his smartphone. All it needed was a coat of a special waterproof paint – and problem solved.

Presumably your roof is fine although be warned: it's only a matter of time before you'll get a howling gale down the Severn Estuary. Oh dear! Your hapless friend with his lovingly-crafted oak gate – do I detect a small note of schadenfreude? In Florida it is not uncommon for high winds to take the roofs off whole cities. If it's not global warming, climate change or a mass shooting, the world is becoming increasingly dangerous, and my pacemaker will not allow me to get off.

Best wishes,

Herbert

December 2015

Letter to Chris Prance, a Friend

Dear Chris,

There has been a murder in New Malden, once the second most peaceful suburb in the UK after Bideford. When I was a Victim Support volunteer, before my stint as desk sergeant in the local police station, I was heavily leaned on to specialise in something or anything – a sort of 'expert' in the group like the second double bass ukulele in your group. I chose homicide in the hope that the scarcity of murders in Kingston would render my assistance so remote as to be negligible, especially with the actual victim no longer in existence. It is just as well I am not a volunteer anymore because I could be run off my feet now.

Let me tell you about my recently-installed handrails (£440 and over a year of planning, ignored emails, reminders and ultimate threats) to stop me breaking my neck on venturing down the terrace steps into the garden. It quite literally now is 'steady as she goes'. When ordering a pair of handrails, for aesthetic reasons I naturally assumed they would be identical. Not so. The left was two inches higher than the right. Naturally, I complained loudly – clearly to good effect. In fact it would be fair to say I *railed* at the asymmetry: the result was the return of the responsible blacksmith, farrier or forger who resected two inches off the higher upright and welded the gap together leaving not a trace.

With best wishes,
Herbert
April 2016

Letter to Michael, his Son

Dear Michael,

With the recent stories in the news of Zika, you might be interested to hear about a case of microcephaly that never was. I recall it was the summer of 1981 or perhaps 1982.

The mother had booked for her first confinement at Charing Cross Hospital (Fulham). The maternity department and special care baby unit were then at the nearby West London Hospital.

All went perfectly well until 35 weeks when she said her baby was moving less. An ultrasound scan showed a breech lie with a BPD[60] of 75mm and estimated head circumference of 26.6mm. The abdominal circumference was normal. The doctor who did the scan added:

> In the light of the above, I think this is a severe microcephalic. The patient asked me my opinion and I told her.

The problem for me was compounded by the fact that we had booked our family holiday the following week. However, I felt that the sooner this baby was delivered the better for everybody. I was not convinced the baby was microcephalic and it would alleviate the parents' distress and uncertainty. Four weeks' prematurity presented no special paediatric difficulty and I promised to be present at the birth regardless of time.

Unfortunately I was unable to persuade the obstetrician to induce labour under epidural analgesia at what was now 36½ weeks. He argued he was not prepared to take risks with a mother in the delivery of a malformed fetus. A breech

---

60. Biparietal diameter, the diameter of the baby's head.

delivery presented no obstetric difficulty since the after-coming head was small and unlikely to get stuck. Moreover, there was a case for not resuscitating a microcephalic baby and for not monitoring the labour. The obstetrician also dismissed my impending holiday as socially irrelevant as the paediatric care would be covered by my colleague Hugh Jolly.

Unfortunately therein lay the rub since we were polarised on a number of issues. Hugh believed passionately in 'bonding' whereas I thought it was bunkum. On his postnatal ward, mothers were urged to sleep with their babies (two fell out of bed); to breastfeed round the clock; bottles of formula milk were banished; and maximum skin-to-skin contact had to take place at all times. On my postnatal ward, thirsty babies could be fed, babies of sleeping mothers were in their cots and there was a nursery where noisy babies could go so that the rest of the ward could get some peace. It all sounds very trivial but in the event turned out to be critical.

With the parents becoming increasingly distraught, the obstetrician reluctantly agreed to induce labour a week later by which time I was away on holiday. The baby, a boy, weighed 2.6kg with a head circumference of 29.5cm. The paediatricians diagnosed severe microcephaly and the 'bonding team' went into full-blown action.

Three days later, the mother had had enough and discharged herself, leaving the baby behind. The social workers placed the baby in foster care where he became the responsibility of the local disability team. The parents refused all contact.

When the little boy was ten weeks old the foster mother had had enough and said she was unable to cope. He was admitted back to Charing Cross on a day on which I was 'on take' and thus he came under my care.

On examination, he was perfectly normal, including his head size, shape and general development. There was absolutely nothing wrong with him. He was in perfect health! I looked up his birth records: nobody had thought to take a photograph but one of Hugh Jolly's juniors had written *small sausage-shaped head*. Now as you know, babies' heads are easily moulded and a case of marked sausage-like moulding had been reported in the journals in a woman with a bicornuate uterus.[61]

The mother was telephoned with the good news and came at once to collect the little boy and take him home. I referred her back to the obstetrician for a salpingogram which confirmed that she did indeed have a bicornuate uterus.

The baby raised many issues, especially by my colleague preaching the holy bonding gospel at every available pulpit like a driven Billy Graham; and with me debunking it in print with titles such as *Mumbo Gumbo*, *The Epoxy Plague* and suchlike. As you can imagine, it was difficult for the junior staff to be loyal to both warring camps but I persuaded the senior registrar to publish it as a case report in the *British Medical Journal* as there was clearly a lesson to be learned.

Love,

Dad

November 2016

---

61. A bicornuate uterus is a womb that has two horns and a heart-shaped cavity.

Letter to Nina Sugarman, a Friend

Dear Nina,

Thank you for your farewell drink before setting off on your long annual migration south for the winter sunshine. For a brief moment I thought it might be Hanukkah. Maybe it was, but unlike Christmas which is always on the same day of the year come rain or shine, Hanukkah is a movable feast, designed by Solomon to save candles. Said to have a thousand wives, the saving must have been immense.

Dinah has always had an *idée fixe* about keeping the Christmas tree up until the 12th day, which is long after all the others in the neighbourhood have been thrown out and the Council has stopped taking away the needle-shedding carcasses free of charge. With no small children, grandchildren or great-grandchildren, I am hoping to forgo the usual arguments, from which I always come off worse, this eco-friendly year by not having a tree at all. Less deforestation, less climate change, less global warming and less greenhouse gas pollution of the atmosphere.

In the interest of an ailing NHS swamped by oldsters falling off ladders, I have stopped clambering up into the loft to fetch stuff I hoped never to see again; and I have stopped heaving myself onto chairs to change a light bulb. Our family is not without 'form' (in police parlance) despite Hitler's evil attempt to wipe it out. My father, ever fearful of getting ripped off by a dodgy tradesman, fell off the garage roof when at 75+ he should really have left the job to a professional. He broke all five toes of one foot and spent a sleepless month in Charing Cross Hospital, each broken toe attached by a cork to a Heath Robinson contraption of wires, pulleys and weights, suffering the dawn, dusk and all-night chorus of coughing, spitting and hawking of the nineteen geriatrics in the other beds. Then my mother, at 85, fell off a chair she had climbed on to clean a window and broke her hip which had to be pinned.

Quickly forgotten in under 24 hours as one is on retiring from one's place of work after 30 years, there are few (if any) of my contemporaries left to keep in touch with. However I still get regular cards at this time of year from the parents of babies I attended, some as long as 45 years ago. One from New Zealand, diagnosed as a case of 'Avoidance Syndrome' by a nutty psychiatrist, is a 45-year-old 'lad' with nothing worse than still wanting to live at home and refusing to flee the nest. I advised his parents to downsize and it worked a treat. Problem solved.

I hope you are enjoying the warm Cape winter and not overburdening yourself with a string of visitors hoping to be waited on hand and foot in true Nina tradition.

With love,

Herbert

December 2016

Letter to Michael, his Son

Dear Michael,

One day you are going to inherit a gold Parker fountain pen. I'd like you to know the provenance of the pen, so bear with me whilst I tell you the story.

Anthony Webber[62] had many desperately severe attacks of asthma as a toddler before we found a solution. The pen was a present from his grateful and immensely relieved parents.

I first saw Anthony at his home in 1968 when he was 10 months old. Anthony's father, Leonard, was a solicitor in Kensington and would now be in his eighties, that's if he is still alive. The family lived in a ground-floor flat in Barons Court and their GP was Dr Watkin in Addison Road. The standard management at the time was Choledyl (an oral theophylline) and Phenergan syrup. The standard hospital regime included intravenous steroids, aminophylline and isoprenaline, and oxygen from free-standing cylinders piped into a tent. Salbutamol and inhalers were not available until 1971.

As the problem was going to need close and prolonged supervision, I offered to see him regularly as an NHS patient at Fulham Hospital where the new Charing Cross Hospital was about to be built. The children's ward was in primitive, temporary hutted accommodation. There was no intensive care, adult or paediatric (in fact it was hard to find intensive care facilities anywhere in London), but we were already pioneering newborn intensive care in my department at Fulham.

---

62. I have changed the name of the patient to protect his identity.

As time went on, it became apparent that his attacks were becoming more severe. We had two other severe asthmatics on the ward at about the same time. One, under my colleague, had prolonged oxygen lack which left her severely brain-damaged. The other stopped having attacks when I had her placed in the care of her grandmother instead of her single mother who was deliberately provoking her spasms.

Anthony however had excellent and loving parents who understandably became increasingly concerned by the extraordinary and unstoppable severity of his attacks. To begin with they appeared to be associated with upper respiratory infections – yet prophylactic antibiotics had no effect at all. I then encouraged the parents to move house on the assumption that he was allergic to something in his surroundings. They moved to Neasden but the change made no difference. They had another child, a sister for Anthony, but this too made no difference. Their house was on my route to Kingsbury Maternity Hospital, so I saw him at home regularly to spare them the journey to Fulham.

By this time, I had worked out that all his attacks occurred, curiously, at monthly intervals. In between his attacks Anthony was perfectly well. Also, they always began with the same innocuous symptoms of an ordinary common cold but followed twenty-four hours later by another devastating attack of asthma with his admission to hospital and every known stop having to be pulled out to save his life.

I asked the parents to bring him in at the earliest sign of a cold when we would start him on oral steroids. I remember our SHO[63] (and a winner of our paediatric prize), seeing this apparently well little boy running round the ward,

---

63. Senior house officer.

doubting the wisdom of admitting an apparently well child and putting him on steroids on such flimsy grounds as a few sniffles – but without steroid treatment he would, within hours, be at death's door.

In sheer desperation, I persuaded his parents to leave him with us for a whole month to see if this would break the cycle of whatever allergy was triggering these attacks; but sure enough he had another attack in my ward when the month was up.

I discussed the problem with several learned colleagues in case there was something I had missed. I went over the problem at length with Archie Norman, an experienced paediatrician at Great Ormond Street, where he looked after asthmatics, and I also asked Professor Soothill, an immunologist from Great Ormond Street, to see him in Fulham, all to no avail.

Anthony's attacks were harrowing. The anguish of the parents who helplessly watched him fight for breath time after time was unimaginable. The most perilous attacks occurred when he was about three years old. The airway obstruction was so intense that oxygen alone was no longer effective and it became necessary to ventilate him for short periods using a Bird respirator which we not only had to borrow but which, in any case, as a pressure-regulated device, was unsuited to overcoming obstructive airway disease.

I forget the exact circumstances of him being ventilated the last time. I think he had collapsed and was intubated and ventilated by the crash-call anaesthetist and put on the Bird ventilator overnight. The spasm eased off after eight or nine hours and I extubated him the next morning. I was due for a weekly session at Moor House School[64] in Oxted that

---

64. Moor House School is a specialist school for children with speech and language difficulties.

afternoon where I received an urgent summons to return to Fulham as it was thought he was once again in severe spasm. It was obvious to me that he had laryngeal obstruction and not bronchial obstruction, due to the prolonged presence of a conventional rubber endotracheal tube instead of a plastic tube. At this very moment, his father walked in, expecting him to have recovered.

The question now was whether to perform a tracheostomy or re-intubate. I remember a hair-raising journey to the operating theatre. The wheels of his cot had not been oiled since it was bought and were firmly rusted. The surgeon and anaesthetist were ready and waiting. We opted for a temporary tracheostomy as the safest option and Anthony made a good recovery.

It was 3½ weeks to the next attack. I arranged an informal case conference of a dozen or more of interested experts, registrars and SHOs at Great Ormond Street in the hope that someone might come up with a useful idea. David Hull, who succeeded Archie Norman soon after, was there as well as several bright up-and-coming senior registrars. Could we prevent the next attack in three weeks?

A registrar from New Zealand by the name of Brent Taylor had seen a case in New Zealand who was cured with prophylactic oral steroids when an attack was due. We had already tried this, using 15mg which is a substantial dose in a 15kg 3-year-old. Brent said they found this insufficient. In New Zealand they were using 80mg to suppress an attack in their patient.

In the absence of any other suggestions, I decided it was worth a try. It meant asking a 3-year-old to swallow 16 tablets! The parents were prepared to try anything as long as it was safe. I gave them a supply of prednisolone and asked them to telephone me at the first sign of a 'cold' when

I would give them further instructions. I forget whether we had the prednisolone made up specially or simply left it to his mother, a sweet, patient lady and excellent mother, to somehow get the tablets down. The awaited telephone call came more or less on the expected day. Anthony was given 80mg, and another 80mg the following day. I held my breath: nothing happened! The allergy did not escalate. The bronchi did not go into spasm. For the first time in eighteen months the expected attack had been completely aborted.

This sequence was to be repeated the following month and again the month after. When three or four expected attacks had been successfully prevented, a semblance of normality at last began to return to the Webber home. No admissions, no intravenous drips, no desperate fight to breathe, no cyanosis, no life support. It was the end of a long chapter of nightmares.

By now David Hull had succeeded Archie Norman at Great Ormond Street. For various reasons, the family and I agreed that if the severe attacks were to return, Anthony would be safer under David Hull at Great Ormond Street, where the intensive care facilities were better, although Charing Cross, Fulham would always be open to them. Our paediatric ward held only memories of unimaginable horrors. Anthony was at long last better and this was an opportunity for a new dawn. The gold Parker pen was a parting gift from his parents in conclusion of a best forgotten chapter.

All went well for many months. He even stopped having yearly follow-ups. I happened to meet David Hull many years later and enquired about Anthony. David had also moved on, first as professor in Nottingham and then as President of the Royal College of Paediatrics and Child Health. He was knighted a year or so later: he is now Professor Sir

David Hull. Apparently, although Anthony had 'grown out' out of his severe allergy, and had been discharged from his asthma clinic, his parents went on giving him 80mg of prednisolone at the first hint of a cold until he was twelve, because nobody told them it was no longer necessary until David happened to see him for an unrelated complaint.

Much – if not all – of the credit should go to Brent Taylor, the young doctor from New Zealand. Brent was later appointed to the chair of paediatrics at the Royal Free Hospital.

I have today Googled Anthony: he is a well-respected solicitor in London, specialising in litigation. He would now be about 50. Whenever I write with my pen I think of him, his family, and their forbearance.

Love,

Dad

January 2017

Letter to Chris Prance, a Friend

Dear Chris,

We are both pushing ninety for better and worse, when glitches of time and lapses of memory are common enough to be considered normal. The trials and tribulations of Christmas, New Year's Eve and 1st Jan are now mercifully consigned to history and things can at last settle down to the normal humdrum existence. We have done the rounds of the charity shops for heavily discounted Christmas cards although I don't expect to be around when the time comes. It is a relief not to have to put up decorations or restore them to the loft when we have a perfectly good box room without the hassle. In fact, I don't understand why we have to have coloured lights etc. when nobody else in the street can be bothered anymore. Most people seem to seize the opportunity to push off somewhere with more snow or sun or both. Carollers are a phenomenon of the past, or perhaps people other than Gareth Malone are an endangered species.

So, having survived Christmas and 1st Jan, my thoughts are now looking, not without trepidation, at Easter. Meanwhile, Dinah has ordered a chairlift although I am perfectly capable of going up and down stairs at my own (snail's) pace, and if needs be driving my lovely car to the High Street provided I don't have to walk too far when I get out. The only problem is that having parked it, I can't walk far.[65] I also pay great heed to the cautionary advice of your GP to proceed in a

---

65. At my suggestion, Dad applied for a 'Blue Badge'. These were once granted on the say-so of the patient's doctor, but now a ridiculous assessment must be performed by a non-medic. Dad struggled to the appointment at the local council where he was seen by an inept and useless official, and was turned down. He was too proud to re-apply or appeal.

'steady' manner and stay on your feet, because I know to my cost that if I fell over I would not be able to get up again without the assistance of someone with more muscle power than any little old lady with a shopping basket on wheels. So, the stairlift is on order: forget the promise that it will be installed the same day. I am not in a hurry but my eyebrows tend to go up without coming down when empty promises are not kept.

I seem to spend a lot more time sleeping – not that I am complaining unless some idiot rings the doorbell and drags me down from upstairs unnecessarily. We have rather given up having visitors. I can only imagine with great admiration how you intend to cope with the annual Norman invasion. I imagine daily sunrise dips in the freezing ocean could be on the back burner where the temperature is less of a shock, and of course you have your ukulele to keep you warm and your fingers in shape.

With best wishes,
Herbert
January 2017

Letter to Chris Prance, a Friend

Dear Chris,

My old bones tell me I am neglecting my best and longest e-pal. As we are both pushing ninety, I know you will understand. It's an age of procrastination, finding excuses for putting things off, and leaving matters for another day in the hope that they will not be needed while ever long grows the list of things to be done. Much as we love our NHS, would it not be great to have a national 'elf service as well? Although I have long admired you as the epitome of resourcefulness, there must be times when even you would be glad to take a well-earned rest from your now traditional commitments.

We gave up holidays a long time ago, having decided home is by far the most comfortable and hassle-free place. With this in mind, we have recently splashed out on a chairlift, which is a lot slower than pounding up and down stairs but saves the effort when the milkman is not at the door and unseemly haste is not the essence. We had a double whammy last week when we were lucky enough to miss the Jehovah's Witnesses on both visits.

Anno Domini and I seem to have spent a lot of time on and off trolleys in outpatient waiting areas. The present system which seems to have been widely adopted is to hide patients in waiting areas cubicled off by plastic curtains and in which they can easily be forgotten. Rumour has it one was not found until next morning. And these are private hospitals. I daren't imagine what it must be like in the NHS.

What with age and sedatives – the maligned midazolam – I can be forgiven for not knowing where I was, and why;

Dinah tells me it was for cannulating and dilating the pancreatic duct, the benefits of which I have yet to feel.

With best wishes,

Herbert

January 2017

Letter to Chris Prance, a Friend

Dear Chris,

I wonder if you are afflicted with my present problem of things disappearing, and if so if you have found a solution. I lost my left slipper for a week which Dinah unexpectedly found between the bed-base and mattress this morning. How did it get there, I wonder? My door keys have gone AWOL for a week, although I have not been out of the house, and the confounded keys are still missing.

I seem to spend most of my day hunting down the backs of sofas and under cupboards in a frantic and futile search for one thing or another which have to be in the house since I have not been out.

I don't believe in ghosts or gremlins and yet still things keep disappearing from under my nose only to reappear in unexpected places. I don't think I am going round the bend, except in my chairlift which has to navigate two sharp bends on its journey. I am perfectly capable of going up and down stairs but the chairlift is too tempting to resist. I certainly find it a blessing at times – simply to flop into a comfortable chair and be effortlessly carried upstairs or downstairs by pushing a button. Three cheers for technology. I wish it could find my keys.

With best wishes,

Herbert

February 2017

Afterword

After Dad retired from clinical paediatrics, he continued to examine for the MB BS finals and for the Royal College of Physicians; he sat on the Vaccine Damage Tribunal; and he performed medicolegal work. And when he relinquished these duties he joined Victim Support and became a volunteer at the local police station. Even in retirement he wanted to reach out to those in need. Dad seldom spoke about what he did at the police station, although an email he sent is telling:

My other occupation, apart from being lazy and reluctantly doing some gardening, is to help out at the local police station. It is not a bit like NYPD. We do not wear bullet-proof vests or shoulder a couple of six-shooting Smith & Wessons. Tomorrow's assignment is to go through CCTV footage, presumably looking for a villain, but the crime rate in our area is low and curiously we don't deal with crime anyway.

He played tennis twice, sometimes thrice, a week until his mid eighties. He was mentally alert and 'switched on' – even at the end of his life.

He enjoyed sending and receiving emails, ever keen that a decent standard of the English language be maintained! Writing to one friend Dad commented: *It is a rare pleasure in this era of declining standards to get a letter that is a model of spelling, grammar and content.*

And what became of Dad's neonatal unit? The special care baby unit that he fought so hard for, fought for its very survival as if it were a premature infant with its own beating heart. I described in the early pages of this book the neonatal unit's move, in 1981, from Charing Cross Hospital to the West London Hospital. Although renowned for its women-centred maternity department from the early 1970s, the West London Hospital sadly closed in 1993 and its maternity services moved to the new Chelsea and Westminster Hospital in Fulham Road. The building was sold and refurbished as self-contained air-conditioned offices. The facade is listed and has been preserved. Thankfully the neonatal unit survived: the unit built, and commanded, by my father lives on at its new site at the Chelsea and Westminster Hospital. The unit is now run by Professor Neena Modi.

Dad infrequently needed medical attention: when he did he would consult a colleague. He would do so on a 'private' basis, not availing himself of NHS care. Until he was in his eighties he rarely consulted a GP. And of course I was on hand, able to advise him or refer him where appropriate. As any doctor would attest, serious medical emergencies always happen at night or at weekends. When Dad suffered his cardiac arrest on an Easter Monday, I called Robin Roberts, a cardiologist friend, who quite literally came to the rescue and saved Dad's life. Robin's skill and expertise gave Dad another twelve years of life, allowing him back onto the tennis court just a few weeks later and, pertinently, enabling him to see his two grandsons mature into young men.

So, despite working for the NHS since its inception and remaining a dedicated employee for forty years, Dad was never once admitted as an NHS patient – that is, until the very end. In March 2017, and now aged eighty-nine, Dad became unwell, battling an infection, and by his own admission he felt it was time to say a final farewell. Our regulatory body discourages us from looking after our own family; thus I stepped aside and his GP admitted him to our local hospital. My goodness! What an eye-opener. The care Dad received was embarrassingly awful – zero medical input, disinterested clinicians and poor nursing care. After watching Dad languish on the NHS ward, I could stand by no more. Above all I felt sadness at this, now, for a man that had given his life to the NHS, working all hours, weekends even when not on call, going into Charing Cross Hospital at all hours. On the fourth day I telephoned a friend, Professor Marcus Reddy, and arranged Dad's transfer to a local private hospital. Here, Dad was superbly looked after by Marcus, aided by another friend, Dr Farid Bazari.

Marcus Reddy is the definition of a perfect doctor – proficient with a superb bedside manner. Dad now benefited from the best care. In due course, a third doctor, Professor Paddy Stone, was brought in and under the assiduous benevolence of these three fine medical men, Dad received skilled, warm and empathic care in the last few days of his long life. He slipped away peacefully seven days later on 20th March.

After Dad's funeral I fired up his computer in case there were important emails that needed my attention. Amongst the various unopened and unread emails, there was a new message from Chris Prance. He and Dad were close friends and had enjoyed a long-running email correspondence (the ones published in the pages of this book are just a selection). This is what Chris had sent:

Dear Herbert,
You have beaten me to it! This is just to say 'goodbye' to my one-time tennis partner, pen pal and sender of wonderfully stimulating and encouraging letters over the past fifteen years or so. It has been a privilege to have had your friendship and the opportunity to share accounts of the various ups and downs of our respective lives. As we are almost twins by age, it can't be all that long before I too gravitate to that mysterious other place where, you never know, we might renew our acquaintance. In the meantime I shall greatly miss your wit, your talent with words and most of all your friendship.
As always,
Chris
23rd March 2017

As Dad's friend Joe Ruston tells us at the beginning of this book, in 2013 he wrote to Dad saying that it had been nice to see him at the funeral of a mutual friend. My father had replied, quoting from Walt Whitman, O Captain! My Captain! Our fearful trip is done.

Herbert Barrie – paediatrician, husband, father and grandfather. You are very much missed.

Michael Barrie
March 2018